EXPERIENCING SURROGACY:
Perspective and Advice from a Surrogate's and Intended Parent's Pregnancy Journey Together

Emily Dubin Field and Melissa Fleck

Published by Van Rye Publishing, LLC
www.vanryepublishing.com

Library of Congress Control Number: 2019950951
ISBN-13: 978-1-7340344-0-0
ISBN-10: 1-7340344-0-8

Dedication

For Ava
This book is for you so that you may know more
about your birth story and how badly Daddy and I
wanted you.
Love, your mommy, Emily

&

For Kevin, Liam, and Harper
Thank you for always supporting my dreams and lifting
me up to help me achieve my goals. You are my reason,
and I love you all so much.
Love, your mom, Melissa

"By coming forward and sharing your story, you don't know the countless lives you change."

—Mariska Hargitay

Contents

Preface

Purpose of This Book

S URROGACY IS A UNIQUE, beautiful, and challenging way to have a baby. Emily, intended parent, and Melissa, gestational surrogate, compiled a list of the ten main stages of the surrogacy process, which they discuss in this book from their individual perspectives. They hope that through you reading about their personal experiences, you will feel informed and supported, whether you are looking into surrogacy as an intended parent or surrogate, are currently involved in your surrogacy, are a professional in the field of fertility and infertility, or are simply curious about surrogacy and want to know more. This is their story, and they hope to make a difference by sharing it.

This book is divided into ten parts. For each part, Emily and Melissa will share their individual perspectives of that particular part of the surrogacy journey. Sometimes intended parents get to hear from former intended parents while surrogates get to hear from former or current surrogates. What makes this book unique is that it gives someone in these roles the opportunity to hear from not only the person in their same role but also from the other side. And if you are neither an intended parent nor a surrogate, it will provide you an opportunity to share in the surrogacy journey from a more well-rounded view, getting both perspectives. This book is intended to be a quick read (because who has time to read something long?).

As a reader of this book, you should note that Emily and Melissa were matched in 2014, and Ava was born in 2015. But the field of assisted reproduction and surrogacy is constantly changing and evolving. So, it is important to keep oneself updated and educated as new developments occur. You should also note that some names and identifying details in this book have been changed to protect the privacy of individuals. And lastly, you should note that this book is the personal experience of the authors. Every person's surrogacy journey is unique, and the relationship among the parties is unique. Not all surrogacies result in a baby, and not all intended parents and surrogates have a relationship similar to the authors'.

Melissa and Emily

Introduction

How Our Pregnancy Journey Began

EMILY (INTENDED PARENT)

Hi, I'm Emily. I'm a mom, thanks to in vitro fertilization (IVF) and surrogacy. It took my husband Gregg and me three years to have our miracle baby—and I definitely believe and feel that she is a miracle! When we decided to try to get pregnant, we automatically assumed that we would be like the majority of our friends and get pregnant fairly quickly. At that time, we had good jobs, had purchased our first home together, had rescued a dog, and had taken several amazing trips around the world. We believed we were ready for a baby, so I went off birth control pills for a few months, stayed fit and healthy, and completed genetic testing.

After close to a year of trying (and even ovulating on our wedding anniversary), we were not pregnant, so I made an appointment with my obstetrician-gynecologist

(OB-GYN). Her first suggestion was to have Gregg's sperm tested and for me to undergo acupuncture sessions. We took her advice and did both. The morphology and motility of Gregg's sperm were a bit abnormal, so my OB-GYN suggested we take the next step and referred us to a reproductive endocrinologist (RE), Dr. Ben-Ozer (Dr. B).

We made our appointment with Dr. B right away (we are very on-it people!). Gregg was extremely distraught that he could be the reason for our infertility, and understandably so. We decided to perform an insemination as our first step. When we saw Dr. B, she could tell that I was getting close to ovulating, so we decided to just go through with it and attempt it then. According to her, washing Gregg's sperm would help our chances. Although we were hopeful, I ultimately got my period.

At our next appointment with Dr. B, she advised that it was now *my* turn to go in for a series of tests. I was shocked. I asked, "Why? I thought Gregg has the problem, not me." She reassured me that she just wanted to be certain there were no issues on my side before we attempted anything else. I was really hesitant and not in support of this tactic; after all, we had already determined what the issue was, right? But after the initial shock and denial that I actually might be part of the problem wore off, I finally made the rational decision to listen to all of Dr. B's recommendations and be tested. And it turned out that I *was* the real issue—not Gregg! Although those results made my husband feel relieved about himself, I was absolutely devastated. Thankfully, Gregg quickly began supporting me during the next stressful stages of our journey. Marriages can be tested during trying times, so it was crucial to Gregg and me that our relationship remain strong. We truly were a team—in this together.

Infertility treatments are not fun! I had more vials of blood drawn than I could even count; two to three doctor's appointments per week; countless vaginal ultrasounds; a hysterosalpingogram (HSG) procedure, which they had to perform twice because the first time it didn't work properly; multiple medicated intrauterine inseminations (IUIs); multiple rounds of IVF, which was very rare because my follicle-stimulating hormone (FSH) and anti-Müllerian hormone (AMH) levels were bad; cancelled IVF cycles since my follicles weren't responding; failed embryo transfers; a hysteroscopy; biopsies; dozens of supplements to take daily; acupuncture sessions; and certain so-called "fertile" foods to eat, like fertile eggs, green tea, Mama Chia drinks, and more. This process continued month, after month, after month. I vividly remember being at work and having to go into the bathroom a few times per day to insert vaginal suppositories. In addition, I literally could not wear work pants for an entire year because my stomach was so bruised from the shots. I was emotionally, physically, and psychologically exhausted, and despite Gregg's constant support, I now felt totally depressed and defeated. And not to mention the amount of money we had already spent!

When Dr. B eventually mentioned the possibility of surrogacy to us, I immediately responded with a big *NO*. How could I even remotely want or trust someone to carry *our* baby for me? But Dr. B persisted, strongly suggesting that surrogacy was our next and, most likely, final viable option to have a biological child. Gregg sided with her, but it took a bit more rational and emotional convincing before I was willing to commit to this concept. In the end, however, the most important thing was a baby. I firmly believe that babies come from your heart, so my not carrying the baby would in NO WAY make me less of a mother. I had to get over the thoughts that were in my mind of giving birth to a baby and turn my focus to being (and becoming) a mom. Oh, and we also had to figure out how we would come up with an additional $120,000 plus! We had already spent $80,000!

Before we tried to conceive, I was adamant that I would never do IVF. But when faced with IVF being my only option on the road to our biological baby, my beliefs ultimately changed. The same was true for surrogacy. But our journey through disappointments and failures ultimately led me to the place of being able to say yes to surrogacy. During this period of indecision, Dr. B also suggested that we consult with an adoption attorney, which we did. In the end, Gregg and I fought HARD to make our precious few embryos and together decided that we would save adoption as our last option for a child if surrogacy did not work. We interviewed three different surrogacy agencies over the next few months until deciding on the agency we would work with to find us our perfect surrogate.

Emily

* * *

MELISSA
(GESTATIONAL SURROGATE)

Hi, I'm Melissa. I'm married to Kevin and am a mom to two kids. I loved being pregnant, and I became pregnant very easily both times. I had full-term pregnancies. My husband and I decided that two kids was just right for our family, and we were not going to have any more; however, I still felt that I wanted to be pregnant again, so I started looking into becoming a surrogate. A coworker of mine had been a surrogate, and she referred me to the agency that she worked with. When I approached my husband, Kevin, with the idea that I was interested in becoming a surrogate, he did not understand surrogacy or why I would possibly want to do it. He finally told me that if I still wanted to be a surrogate in one year, we could talk about it more at that time.

One year went by, and I knew that I wanted to do this. Kevin supported me, though cautiously, since he was concerned about my health and what seemed like taking an unnecessary risk. He was also worried about what possible impact the pregnancy could have on our family, as our children were only ages one and three and still required constant care. But because I could not let go of the idea of being a surrogate, even after a year of researching and learning, he ultimately decided to take the journey with me. I applied with the agency that my coworker had used. I had to complete a long written application, submit my medical records from my pregnancies, have a criminal background check done (as well as one on Kevin), have an interview, talk to several agency members, go in for psychological testing, and have a preliminary medical screening.

I was very excited after my application was accepted, but during my phone interview, I discovered that there were still many things left in order to be fully accepted as a surrogate. Everything about this stage is considered the screening process, so I was cautiously optimistic throughout this entire phase. I knew nothing would come up in my background check; I was fairly certain I would pass the psychological testing; and from everything I knew, my pregnancies were textbook. But what if the agency found something in my records that I didn't remember that would disqualify me? Or what if my health insurance wasn't surrogacy-friendly? What if something *did* show up on my psych test? All of these things were in the back of my mind as I was gathering and sending in all of these documents. Once everything was complete, and I was told that I had been officially accepted, I was ecstatic to begin reviewing profiles of couples seeking a surrogate.

Melissa

Receiving Each Other's Profile

"The greatest good is what we do for one another."
—Mother Theresa

EMILY'S PERSPECTIVE

After Gregg and I signed with a surrogacy agency, our next step was to create our profile. We wrote about how we met, where we lived, our ages, our jobs, our families, our friends, our support system, and, of course, our infertility struggles. Except for the last item, we felt like we were creating a profile for an online dating site, which was funny to us since that is how we met. Part of our profile included a letter to our future surrogate. We also included photos that were special to and representative of us. We worked with the amazing case manager at our agency, Joanne, to make our profile the best it could be. We wanted to be sure to attract the perfect surrogate for us.

After our profile was done, then came the hardest part: the waiting. Our agency warned us that it could take anywhere from two to six months to be matched. We were told that we would receive the profile of a potential surrogate for us via email. Being patient is not my strong suit, so I found myself emailing the agency every few weeks or so to check on the status of when we might be sent a potential match. In this time of waiting, there was nothing else to do but wait.

After four very long months, we were sent an initial profile of a potential surrogate. Unfortunately, this particular surrogate was not medically cleared to carry twins, and we were not sure at the time if we would transfer one embryo or two embryos (which could lead to twins). It was hard to say *no* to this surrogate without knowing when we would receive the next surrogate profile. We had sent Dr. B the profile of this surrogate, and we spoke to Dr. B on the phone; she agreed with our sentiments about not choosing this surrogate. So, this made us feel a lot better about our decision. And, ultimately, while waiting is hard, we had already spent *so* much time on our journey to a baby that Gregg and I 100 percent agreed that we would wait for the perfect surrogate for us. So, we declined to work with that surrogate, and we then waited for another anxious month before we finally received another profile.

We were sent Melissa's profile on a Friday afternoon. Gregg and I were both at work when we received the email from our agency. I got butterflies in my stomach and looked at the email immediately. Our agency instructed us to review it over the weekend, and then get back to them on Monday. Well, after months of anticipation and disappointment, Gregg and I couldn't wait until we were home together that weekend. We immediately got on the phone with each other and reviewed the profile together—and we both instantly knew that she was "the one." Having no doubts or reasons to wait until Monday, we notified our agency that same Friday.

So, how did we determine that Melissa was "the one?" Well, just like our own profile, Melissa had also written a letter—to her future intended parents. In her letter, she mentioned her marriage to her husband, Kevin, and how supportive and loving he is. She spoke of her two children, Liam and Harper, including their ages and interests; how close she is to her parents, both literally and figuratively; her close-knit group of friends; where she lives and her career; and, most important, why she decided to become a surrogate. Her profile also included medical information about her previous pregnancies and births, her beliefs on termination and reduction, and the type of relationship she wanted with the intended parents and their future child. Just as we had, she included photos of herself, alone and surrounded by her family. One particular photo still stands out in my mind: it's a shot of Melissa, Kevin, Liam, and Harper outside under a tree. Gregg and I could just feel through that image the love they all shared for one another—one more reason we knew Melissa was the right woman to help our own family grow.

The way our particular agency works is that, when we were sent Melissa's profile, we already knew that she wanted to work with us: the surrogate chooses first. So, all we needed to do to continue the process was accept her. When we had interviewed surrogacy agencies to decide which one to use, we learned that they can arrange the matching part differently. Some agencies have the intended parents choose first, then the surrogate. We really liked having the surrogate choose first because we felt that it gave our surrogate ownership into whom she wanted to help make a family. It also made it less stressful for us, since we did not have to deal with considering surrogates who would not want to work with us.

After we accepted Melissa's offer, we scheduled a time for all four of us to have a conference call, and we also exchanged text messages. Gregg and I were nervous for our first call. We weren't sure exactly what we would speak about. We were in the car on the way to my cousin's wedding when we called Melissa and Kevin. We told them that we only had a limited amount of time to chat, as we were getting close to the wedding. We spoke about each of our plans for the weekend, and I also told Melissa about Dr. B and her office so that she felt comfortable when she would go there. We noticed that Kevin was more talkative on the phone than Melissa and assumed it was because she was as nervous as we were.

Melissa's next step was to get medically cleared by our fertility doctor. After this was completed, the four of us would then meet in person with the psychologist who worked with our agency for our official "match meeting," where we would all ultimately decide if we wanted to commit to moving forward together.

* * *

MELISSA'S PERSPECTIVE

The entire process from application through screening moved fairly quickly for me. I applied in January and was matched in March. While I was anxious and excited to finally start reading profiles, I could not believe that I was actually starting the matching process! Emily and Gregg's profile was the first one I received, and I was moved by their story and drawn to them immediately. My husband's reaction was very strong as well; honestly, even stronger than mine. He read their profile, leaned back in his chair, took a deep breath, and said, "Wow. This is our couple."

I, however, was not as positive—for whatever reason, I felt hesitant. Knowing how the agency matches couples and surrogates, I had been expecting to receive three or more profiles, review them all, and then pick one. Something was telling me not to make a decision until I read a few more profiles. In my heart, I knew I wanted to work with Emily and Gregg; but my head was telling me that in order to make a more informed decision, I needed to examine a few more. Upon my request, the agency sent me two more profiles. While their stories were heartbreaking as well, I did not feel that immediate draw to them like I did with the first profile. I emailed our match coordinator and let her know that I could not wait to work with Emily and Gregg!

EXPERIENCING SURROGACY

* * *

2

The Match Meeting

*"Sometimes the people around you don't understand
your journey. They don't need to—it's not for them."*
—Joubert Botha

EMILY'S PERSPECTIVE

Melissa was medically cleared by our fertility doctor, Dr.
B, who gave her the honorary title of a "fertility Olympian." Dr. B had specifically told us that she would not
approve a surrogate for us whom she would not approve
for her own sister. This assurance lifted a lot of stress
from us because we trusted and loved our doctor so much.
Dr. B had been through our long and painful infertility
journey with us, and we felt secure in the knowledge that
she was still invested in us during this process.

Once the clearance was completed, our in-person
match meeting was scheduled. The psychologist from the
agency, Elaine, led this meeting at her office in Santa
Monica. Although we had already spoken on the phone
with Melissa and Kevin, and I had been texting with
Melissa, this would be the first time that we would meet

face-to-face. Gregg and I were both extremely nervous and anxious to meet them, as somehow it made it seem even more real. I was going to get to meet the woman who would carry my child and give birth to her. What?! And no less important, I would also meet her husband, who was hopefully going to be supporting and loving her throughout the entire process.

I wasn't sure if I should bring something for Melissa and, if so, what to bring. The whole financial aspect of surrogacy made me uncomfortable. I never wanted our surrogate to think we had all of this money (which we don't), but I didn't want to insult her either, so I didn't want to bring her something that would be regarded as too much or too little. I finally decided to bring her a nice orchid plant. But in my heart, all I wanted to do was shower her with gifts. I really could not believe that she was willing and hoping to carry a baby for me!

Elaine had Gregg and I arrive at her office a little early for the meeting so that we could have an initial chat. She wanted to ensure that, during the meeting, she covered some of the topics that we felt were important to address in the upcoming conversation. We would soon be signing legal contracts, but an in-person meeting with our potential surrogate allowed us to talk face-to-face about some of the more challenging aspects, such as termination and reduction. We needed to be certain that all four of us—including Kevin, Melissa's husband—were on the exact same page regarding these issues before starting the surrogacy process.

When Melissa and Kevin arrived, Melissa walked in

first and had a big smile on her face. My first thoughts were: *She looks just like her photos.* Phew! *She's in shape and not overweight.* Phew! It really was like a dating website. *She has a warmth about her.* Phew! We immediately gave each other a big hug. Her husband, Kevin, had a protective air about him—a tangible vibe of, "Hey, this is my wife, and I will make sure that she is protected throughout this whole process!" Rather than being put off by his unspoken warning, I actually really liked that about him. I could tell instantly that Melissa was his #1, which is exactly how it should be. I knew that Gregg would feel the exact same if our positions had been reversed.

Elaine instructed us to sit across from each other, and she then guided us in a wonderful discussion. Our conversation covered why Melissa wanted to be a surrogate, any concerns each of us might still have, how Melissa and Kevin's families felt about Melissa committing to this, what abnormalities of the baby we would terminate or reduce for, the type of relationship we all wanted, and more. Melissa revealed to us that she really had to educate her parents about what surrogacy is. Her mom initially thought that Melissa would be giving away one of her grandchildren. But, after some more clarification, her mom was ultimately very supportive.

All of Kevin's questions and comments rightly centered around Melissa, showing us how much he loved her and their own children and how protective he felt. Gregg and I told him that Melissa would remain the most important person in all of this, and we immediately felt very protective over her as well. We were aware that

Melissa understood the risks associated with surrogacy and that she wanted to do this of her own free will, and from day one we never wanted this experience to be anything that could harm Melissa in any way. Once Kevin heard us say this, his demeanor visibly changed.

After the meeting, Elaine suggested that we should treat Melissa and Kevin to a meal. Again, we didn't want to pick a fancy, expensive restaurant or something that was too low-key. We decided on a nice, fun, and kind-of-trendy Mexican restaurant in Santa Monica. I figured that we could be seated at a comfy table and that the restaurant would be louder versus quiet, so we might feel more comfortable having a personal conversation. We also ordered margaritas to help alleviate any of the remaining uneasiness we were still feeling during this initial encounter.

During dinner, Gregg and I learned more about Melissa and Kevin's jobs and their kids. Melissa further explained her feelings regarding wanting to be a surrogate. Although she wanted to be pregnant again, she didn't want another child, which was an alien concept to us. She also revealed that she had known exactly what sex each of her children were going to be and that, if she ever had a third, she felt it would be a girl. Because we knew that we would be transferring a female embryo, things continued to feel even more right. (For those of you wondering, during IVF, we did preimplantation genetic diagnosis [PGD] testing on our embryos, and that is how we learned the sex of the embryo.)

* * *

MELISSA'S PERSPECTIVE

Our match meeting happened on a Thursday evening at the end of March 2014. My husband, Kevin, and I made the short drive to Santa Monica to the office of our counselor/psychologist, Elaine, who had been assigned to us by our agency, so she could be there to facilitate the meeting. I felt pretty comfortable with Elaine by this point, as I had met her in person a few times for my psychological testing and at support group meetings. One great thing about the agency I chose is that they offer monthly support-group meetings for the surrogates, which are conducted by Elaine. Not only is it great to connect and talk with surrogates who are going through or have been through similar situations as you, but it is also great to get that monthly face time with your counselor to build rapport.

I can honestly say I have never been more nervous in my life. It was such a strange thing to prepare for—a meeting like this is like nothing you have ever experienced, and there really is no way to explain it other than equal parts job interview, psychoanalysis, and first date. I knew that the best and *only* thing to do was to just be myself. Emily and Gregg needed to know exactly who I was so they could be confident that they could trust me to carry their child. No pressure, right?

My husband and I arrived and were informed that Elaine was chatting with Emily and Gregg first and that she would call us in when they were ready. Although the wait felt like hours, in reality, it was only fifteen minutes or so. I could not believe that Emily and Gregg were in the next room! The nerves were unbelievable at this point, and my husband and I did everything we could to keep each other feeling calm and collected.

Elaine finally came out to greet us, and she walked us into the room to officially meet Emily and Gregg. Everything we knew about them was from their profile and a few email exchanges, so actually having them in front of us felt like meeting a celebrity for the first time. When I first saw them, I knew immediately that they were the couple for us. Emily is beautiful and exudes warmth, and Gregg has this incredibly sweet and gentle smile—when the two of them are together, there is an unmistakable energy. You are somehow drawn to them, and you want to be a part of their world, which is exactly how I felt when I walked into that room and hugged them. I liked them before they even spoke, and I now felt the pressure was fully on for me to establish a good impression.

We all sat down, and Emily and Gregg handed me a beautiful potted orchid. My first thought was, *What a sweet gesture!* This was immediately followed by, *Oh no! Should I have brought them something?!* But, as we all started chatting, my anxiety quickly subsided.

Our counselor was required to ask some of the important and tough questions while she was there to facilitate. I remember feeling like some of the questions had nothing to do with me; I had made the decision when I was starting on this adventure that my role was simple:

carry their baby. I now understand that we all had to be on the same page regarding issues like termination, reduction, and so forth, but in my mind at that time, all of these decisions were 100 percent theirs—their baby, so their call. Yes, I was going to be carrying the baby, and no one can force me to have an abortion since it's my body, but it would be THEIR baby.

Kevin and my biggest question and concern was for our children: how would we explain this process to a three- and a five-year-old? Would they even understand? Elaine gave us some great tips on how to explain it to them, and she made it clear the importance of having our kids meet Emily and Gregg. They were willing to do so, which helped ease our worries. We then moved on to questions regarding frequency and duration of contact with one another during the surrogacy process. We all agreed to let the relationship progress naturally, and we decided not to put any guidelines on how often we needed to communicate or, after the baby was born, how often I received updates. It was a perfect match, as we were all on the same page about everything.

When the meeting concluded, Emily, Gregg, Kevin, and I went to dinner to get to know each other better in a less formal setting. We left the office, and the second we closed our car doors, Kevin said, "I get it. I know now why you want to do this, and I want to, too—for them." Although my husband had been supportive of my decision to become a surrogate, he admittedly had not fully understood my need/want to do so until that moment. After meeting Emily and Gregg and realizing that there are amazing people in the world like them who want nothing more than a child, he got it. He was all in.

At dinner, the four of us took the time to get to know each other as people—not as surrogate and intended parents. We purposely didn't talk about surrogacy expectations during the journey. Instead, we discussed our families, where we grew up, where we went to college, our jobs, and so forth. We each had a margarita to help us relax, and the conversation flowed naturally. I feel this is a very important part of the match meeting—to spend at least some quality time together *not* talking about surrogacy. This journey is not always easy, and you need to know that you are in it with people whom you trust and who have your back. Without that foundation established beforehand, I believe that things could have become very difficult and awkward later on as different situations come up.

Despite our resolve to not discuss the surrogacy, at one point, the conversation inevitably shifted to embryos. We learned that Emily and Gregg had three genetically tested embryos ready to go. I knew next to nothing about IVF at that time, so I was fascinated by the process. They explained that they knew the sex of all of their embryos, and I was floored. I was amazed that technology had come this far! Emily then coyly asked, "So . . . we already know the sex of the baby we will be having. Do you want to know?" I replied, "I already know. I have known with every ounce of my being that if I had another baby, it would be a girl." Their jaws dropped to the floor—mostly, I'm sure, because of how confident I sounded.

They already knew that both embryos they would be transferring were girls. I think we all took that as the final sign that this match was meant to be!

* * *

3

Signing Legal Contracts

"Things often get tougher before they get easier. Stay strong, be positive. We all struggle sometimes. Your struggle is part of your story."
—Unknown

EMILY'S PERSPECTIVE

After our in-person match meeting, Gregg and I notified our agency that we wanted to move forward with Melissa. Once Melissa and Kevin did the same, the match was finalized, and we began the legal contract. We officially retained our attorney, Andy, and paid our first chunk of money to him. At this point, it felt like we were using Monopoly money with how much we were spending on everything.

It took Andy a few weeks to draft our contract, which we were shocked to find was close to sixty pages! There was the main Gestational Carrier Agreement; Exhibit A, which detailed all of the money and terms that the surrogate would be getting; the Zika Virus Addendum; and an HIV Waiver. We printed all four of them so that we could better review them together. Although Gregg himself is an attorney, there were a lot of aspects of the contract that were totally foreign to him. We reviewed the contract as best we could, yet we did not feel fully comfortable with our understanding of it. We decided to err on the side of caution and scheduled a formal consultation with Andy on the phone.

Our main questions and concerns involved the parts in the contract that detailed termination and reduction. I was aware of this aspect of surrogacy, but it was really not discussed much at all until we saw it in the contract (or if it had been mentioned, I was probably too overwhelmed by everything else to hear and comprehend it). Although it was *our* baby, it was *her* body; ultimately, we could not force Melissa to do anything.

We had been through so incredibly much in getting to this point—what with disappointment after disappointment and spending more than $80,000 already with $120,000 more to go—and felt increasingly anxious for a healthy baby. Although we had taken the precaution of genetically testing the embryos for potential chromosomal abnormalities, there was always the slight chance that something could be wrong. I recall several freak-out moments of not being positive if I could continue to move forward, knowing that I had no legal control over the surrogate's body. This is why being matched with a surrogate who 100 percent agrees with your personal beliefs on termination and reduction is critical! We knew from our discussions with Melissa and Kevin that they shared our beliefs, but seeing it written out in detail in our contract made me feel hesitant and worried.

Andy carefully listened to our concerns, and he ultimately rephrased the language in the contract to make us feel more comfortable. Knowing that our attorney was truly on our team and wanted the best for us made a huge difference. Yet my personal fears about the health of the baby and Melissa continued with me until more than three months *after* Ava was born and Melissa's health had recovered—it was only then that I truly was able to take a deep breath and let go of my worries.

Once both parties agreed to the contract, we each notarized it. The entire process took about six weeks, partly because Melissa's attorney was out of town for a week. Once the contract was notarized, Andy issued legal clearance to the clinic. Melissa could officially begin the process with our fertility doctor, Dr. B, to prepare her uterus for our baby! (For those of you unfamiliar with this process, basically, a surrogate has to take certain hormones to get her uterus ready for the embryo to be able to implant.)

* * *

MELISSA'S PERSPECTIVE

Signing the surrogacy contract was an easy process—for us, anyway. When our attorney received the contract, he called us and went over it line by line. He had been practicing Surrogacy Law for quite some time, so I trusted him to know what was "normal" for a contract.

Nothing in it surprised me, really. All of the restrictions were typical pregnancy restrictions: no raw fish, no nicotine, no hot tubs, and so forth. I already knew about my travel restrictions as well: I could not leave California after I hit twenty-four weeks, to avoid me possibly going into labor in another state, where our contract could become null and void. We mutually agreed to change some wording on a few items that our lawyer wanted clarified for my protection. We sent our draft back to Emily and Gregg's lawyer, and all was good as we waited for everything to be notarized and finalized.

4

The Embryo Transfer

"We loved you before we knew you. Even when there was just hope for you, we loved you."
—Unknown

EMILY'S PERSPECTIVE

Melissa, a.k.a. the fertility Olympian, was now ready for the embryo transfer after being monitored for about two months. We were finally at the part of the journey that I could help Melissa with—at this point, I considered myself the "professional" regarding IVF. Melissa, on the other hand, was a first-time surrogate who had conceived her own children the "natural" way and was unfamiliar with the difficult schedule of hormones, shots, and supplements. I was able to give her tips on this process based on my extensive experience, such as to ice the abdominal area where the shots would go a few minutes before a shot.

Dr. B had been closely monitoring Melissa every few days, and it was now time to schedule the embryo transfer. Melissa only lives about forty-five minutes away from me, and I thought it might be nice to spend some time together before the transfer. She agreed, so I drove to her neighborhood, and we had our nails done (pink, of course, because we knew the embryo was a girl) and went to lunch afterward. We were still getting to know each other, and it remained essential to me that Melissa felt good about our relationship.

Although everything else was already settled, Gregg and I were still dragging our feet on one issue: if we would transfer one embryo or two. We knew that Melissa was medically cleared to carry twins and that she had agreed to this possibility as part of our match. But we were so torn; after everything we had been through, we wanted to give ourselves the best chance possible, on the *first* try with Melissa, to get a baby. On the flip side, we also were extremely concerned about the risks of premature birth and poor health of twins, plus the reality of becoming parents to twins.

Gregg and I reserved our decision about how many embryos to transfer until literally the night before the embryo transfer, when Dr. B contacted us to learn what our decision was so that she could inform the lab of how many embryos to thaw from the freezer. One of our embryos was a lower-quality embryo (genetically tested, but graded lower), and we believed that we would never transfer that embryo by itself. After going back and forth, and back and forth again, we ultimately decided to transfer one good-quality embryo along with the lower-quality embryo: two girls. Dr. B candidly reminded us there was still a chance that *neither* embryo would take, so we had to be prepared for that possibility.

On the morning of the transfer, I was so nervous. One good sign was that the date of our embryo transfer wound up falling on the anniversary date of when my parents met, especially meaningful to me since our baby would be named in my dad's memory. Gregg and I arrived early, as we wanted to double-check that all of the necessary paperwork was done properly. My mom came, too. I felt as reassured and as comforted as possible having my core family with me. Melissa and Kevin then arrived. We had brought a small gift for Melissa: a handwritten card, some magazines, snacks, and a gift card so that Kevin could bring in dinner one night during her required bed rest. We waited for a little bit, and it was then our turn! My mom remained in the waiting room while the four of us went in for the procedure.

Melissa and Kevin entered the room first. We were then called in and had to don gowns, hairnets, and booties. Gregg, Kevin, and I were all sitting at the left side of Melissa. On Melissa's right side was a monitor where we could see her uterus (and eventually the catheter that was holding our embryos). The embryologist came into the room with a long tube that held our embryos in it, which seemed crazy! She told us that she felt privileged to be our child(ren)'s first babysitter, and we were touched by her sweet statement.

We were all in the room as we saw the two embryos placed into Melissa and took photos and videotaped the process. The actual transfer was fairly quick; we spent most of the time in the room waiting before and after. I tried to stay present, but it was hard to accomplish that; although we knew what this process would be like because we had tried an embryo transfer with me, it felt completely different and surreal seeing Melissa, whom we still barely knew, lying there with our precious embryos placed into her uterus. Like during our previous transfers, Dr. B asked if she could say a prayer with us. We had always loved how incredible and personal Dr. B was, and we were willing to take any and ALL prayers we could get.

After the transfer, Melissa was required to remain lying down. I remember asking Melissa if I could rub her feet or do anything at all for her. It was at that moment that I started to fall in love with Melissa. I was in total awe that there was a woman like her who would do something like this for people who were, in reality, complete strangers. I still felt overwhelmed knowing that I was trusting and feeling such strong emotions toward a woman whom I barely knew. All too soon, it was time to leave. Melissa was wheeled out to her car and driven home by Kevin. Gregg, my mom, and I went to lunch. The ten-day wait would now begin!

The Embryo Transfer

* * *

MELISSA'S PERSPECTIVE

Leading up to the embryo transfer, I had been on a series
of medications that help prepare the body to accept the
embryo. All of these were injected. I had never given
myself a shot of anything before, so this was a new
venture for me.

The first medication I went on was Lupron, which
shuts down your menstrual cycle. This was a small needle
injected into the stomach that I was able to easily do
myself. I then added on estrogen, which is what thickens
the lining of your uterus. This was an intramuscular shot
done in the buttocks every two to three days. Finally,
about a week before the transfer, we added on progesterone, which is the pregnancy hormone. We were transferring a five-day embryo, so we needed to trick my body
into thinking it was already pregnant so it would accept
the embryo. The progesterone would continue well into
the pregnancy as well, to keep my levels up. This, too,
was intramuscular.

Unfortunately (or fortunately?) for me, I was never
able to get the angle right to be able to administer these
medications myself, so my husband or my mom did them
for me. I didn't have much pain associated with the
injections, and my body responded well. But once we
started the progesterone, my body acted like it was
pregnant: I was tired, and my breasts were tender and
sore. During the course of the injections, I had lab work

done at least once a week to check my levels so that the doctor could adjust my medications as needed.

I was aware going into the transfer that we would be transferring two embryos and that it could mean a twin pregnancy if both embryos worked. I was so naïve; the thought of twins never really felt like a concern, even though it absolutely should have been. I was just so excited and anxious for the transfer itself! At this point, I had been on medication for about a month to be ready for this next step. I was given explicit instructions to arrive with a full bladder, and by the time we got to the clinic, I was unbelievably uncomfortable. Kevin and I walked into the waiting area, where we saw Emily, Gregg, and Emily's mom, Lois. I remember that there was lots of small talk in the waiting room, but to this day, I cannot recall a single thing we talked about—my mind was too distracted by my bladder!

It seemed like an eternity before we were finally called back for the procedure. While Emily and Gregg waited outside, I put a gown on, and the nurse checked how full my bladder was—a bit too full, as it turned out. Thankfully, the nurse allowed me to empty it a bit so that I could be more comfortable. She also gave me Valium to ensure that every muscle in my body would be fully relaxed when they transferred the embryo. Once I was set up on the table, Emily and Gregg were allowed in. I was a bit nervous as I didn't know what to expect, but they were all smiles and so excited. I didn't want my nerves to get in the way, so I put on my brave face. Then Dr. B came in and asked for permission to say a little prayer over us.

While I am not a very religious person, I thought that it was incredibly touching how much she truly cares about all of her patients.

The actual transfer was quick and easy—almost anti-climactic after all the prep work. Honestly, the most discomfort I felt that day was from my full bladder. The best part was having everything visible on the monitor right next to me. We could witness everything the doctor was doing, including seeing her gently place those two tiny embryos right in my uterus. The whole procedure took only a couple of minutes, and I was somewhat shocked at how uneventful it seemed.

Kevin drove me home, where I was placed on strict bed rest for three days. I could only go up and down my stairs once throughout the course of the day, which was incredibly difficult for me. Granted, I had wonderful support at home; between Kevin and my parents, I was very well taken care of. The roughest part of this involved denying my own children, who were three and five years old. Having them running around or wanting Mommy to make them dinner or give them a bath was difficult, especially since I felt completely fine. But I knew that what I was doing was important and, in the grand scheme of things, lounging on the couch for three days was not going to hurt anyone.

* * *

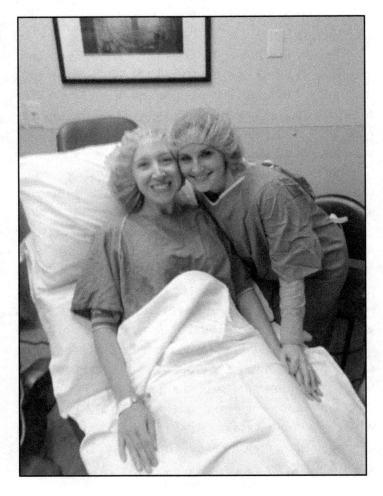

5

The Blood Test to Confirm Pregnancy

"Even miracles take a little time."
—The Fairy Godmother

EMILY'S PERSPECTIVE

Ten days felt like forever! Gregg and I decided that the only way to stay sane was to keep ourselves busy. Our sanity was tested when, the day after the transfer, we were inadvertently told that it did not work. We were distraught. We called Dr. B to ask her if she had heard the same thing. She assured us that it was impossible to have been provided that news, and she encouraged us to stay positive. We had checked in with Melissa to make sure she was ok, and she dismissed the error even more easily than we did. So, we stuck to our ten-day plan. We worked full days, then dined at a new restaurant every night. Although it was not something that we normally would do, we strongly felt the need to say prayers every night together until day ten finally arrived.

Gregg and I both took that day off from work. Our doctor had told us that she would be calling us in the afternoon, so we made plans with the intention of having as relaxing a day as possible. We decided that we would go to breakfast, get massages, and then go to the beach. My mom was the only one who knew about the expected call, and she was planning on coming over to our house that afternoon to either celebrate or mourn with us. Despite our intentions, Gregg and I could barely eat anything at breakfast and were unable to relax during our massages. While driving on the way to the beach, the phone rang: it was our doctor's office. It was only noon. It wasn't yet the afternoon, like when we were told she would call.

I will *never* forget that call. We answered the phone, and Dr. B said excitedly, "So, do you want to wait until this afternoon for me to tell you that you are pregnant?" We were literally driving on a freeway overpass, and both of us started to cry and freak out. (I thought I cried a lot, but Gregg cried the rest of the day and night!) Somehow, Gregg managed to safely exit the freeway, and we pulled into a random strip mall parking lot. I was totally shocked! Dr. B then asked if we wanted her to call Melissa and reveal the results, but we told her that we wanted to be the ones to share the good news. I called Melissa on speakerphone, and she picked up the phone with an uncertain quaver in her voice, "Hi, guys . . ." I shouted, "We are pregnant!"

We spoke for a little bit on the phone. Although I could not recall what we talked about because of all the excitement, I was happy to find out that Gregg had recorded our conversation on his phone so that we could preserve that special moment. While I had called Melissa on my phone, Gregg had been recording us from his phone. I was in such a state of shock at the time that I didn't even realize he was preserving that special moment, but I'm glad that he did.

We then (somehow) managed to drive home, deciding how we would tell my mom, who was scheduled to come over in a few hours. My mom still thought that we would not be hearing from our doctor until later, so we knew she would not be expecting any news yet. We had not previously planned anything because we did not know if the embryo transfer would work, and we had not wanted to jinx anything.

When we arrived home, we found a white T-shirt, wrote "I'm going to be a big sister" on it, and put it on our dog, Dixie. Gregg and I then hid upstairs with the video camera ready. My mom walked into our house, saw our dog, and asked, "Dixie, what are you wearing?" My mom moved closer to Dixie and read the shirt as we approached her with the video camera. My mom, my rock, had suffered through our infertility with us—she had witnessed everything that I had gone through, physically, emotionally, and spiritually—and she started to cry. We then called my grandmother to tell her the good news, and we drove to Gregg's parents' house to surprise them, too. Our families went to dinner that night to celebrate.

Because we had never had a positive pregnancy test before, we were elated, but I was also extremely nervous.

When I came down from my high at the end of the day, my thoughts were focused on the next blood test, which would further confirm the viability of the pregnancy.

* * *

MELISSA'S PERSPECTIVE

The ten-day waiting period from embryo transfer to blood test was excruciating. I had promised myself early on that I would not home-test, for multiple reasons. I did not want the emotional ups and downs of false positives or negatives, and I knew from my support group meetings how common that was. I also strongly felt that I should not be the first one to discover if Emily and Gregg were going to have a baby. It seemed somehow wrong to me, since I believed that the parents should know first.

During my prior pregnancies, I had been very intuitive toward all my symptoms and feelings, but all of the medications I had to take for this pregnancy had messed with that intuition. The progesterone I had been injecting for the few weeks prior to the transfer had made me so tired, and extreme fatigue had been the only first-trimester symptom I remembered an awareness of. Because I really had no clue if I was pregnant, I tried to keep busy and focus on my kids and family to keep my mind off it. I felt a huge amount of pressure for this to work, so distraction was the best way to get through those ten days until I knew for sure if I was pregnant.

I will never forget that phone call with Emily and

Gregg. Kevin, the kids, and I were at the store getting new tires for our boat trailer. Granted, not a very exciting place to get news like this, but luckily the kids and I were in the car while Kevin was talking with the tire people outside. My phone rang, and I saw that it was Emily. My heart dropped, and it then started beating insanely fast. I took a deep breath, answered the phone, and heard a very happy and excited Emily and Gregg on the other end. I immediately assumed that meant good news, but I also knew how incredibly optimistic and upbeat they usually were, so my thoughts changed to, *Wait, what if they are just putting on a brave front for me?* Luckily, they were sweet enough not to keep me in suspense: After a quick *hello* and *how are you?*, they both yelled out, "We're pregnant!" My heart dropped again, my eyes teared up, and I felt this wave of excitement and relief. We had done it—we were pregnant! I now was officially a surrogate.

* * *

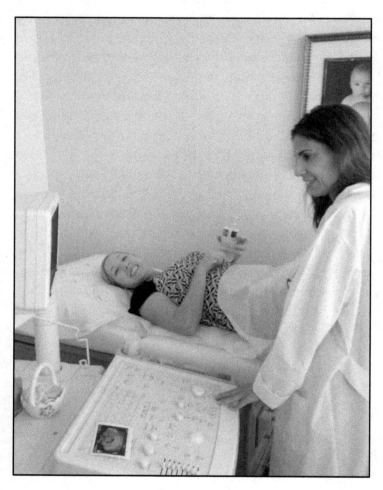

6

The Doctor Appointments

*"Sometimes, when making something precious,
beautiful, and unique, it takes an extra helping hand."*
—Unknown

EMILY'S PERSPECTIVE

Dr. B only monitored Melissa for the first trimester. I had
wanted Dr. B to monitor Melissa for the entire pregnancy,
primarily because she was our doctor and we trusted her.
We knew her; she knew us. But at the start of the second
trimester, as is the standard procedure in surrogacy,
Melissa was released to her own OB-GYN, Dr. N, who
had delivered both of Melissa's kids. We researched him
and discovered great things about him, including that he
was with a hospital that offered a Neonatal Intensive Care
Unit (NICU). But what still bothered me was that we did
not know him, so he did not know us. He only knew
Melissa.

All the first-trimester appointments with Dr. B were
thankfully uneventful, which was so different than all the
appointments with her while I was going through my

fertility treatments. The most memorable for me was the heartbeat appointment, which was truly incredible. There was *one* strong heartbeat, which dismissed any fears of there being twins. Seeing the flicker of the heart on the monitor and then hearing the heartbeat was amazing. I was in awe of Melissa and our doctor, who both had made this possible for us.

Back when we were choosing a surrogate, it had been critical to Gregg and me that she live at least fairly close to us. If this meant that we had to wait longer to be matched with someone, we were willing to wait. Heck, it had already taken us years to have a baby—what was a few more months if it meant being able to attend as many of the medical appointments as possible? This would help us feel a tiny bit more in control of a pregnancy that, in reality, we had little to no control over. With only one exception, Gregg and I attended every single appointment with Dr. B and Dr. N. We only missed that one because we were abroad for our babymoon; and for that one, we made sure to send my mom to be our eyes and ears.

At each appointment, when Melissa was called in, we would give her some time to herself to get weighed and so forth. We didn't want her to feel that we were completely up in her business—yet we wanted to know everything! Then, we would get called into the room before the doctor came in. We always had full rooms at our appointments: at the minimum, it would be Melissa, Gregg, and me. Sometimes the group would include Kevin, sometimes my mom, and one time even Melissa's mom. I wanted to feel as much a part of this pregnancy as possible, which is why I went to all the appointments.

For most of these appointments, the nurses and ultrasound technicians would know who Gregg and I were. It indicated our status in the chart, but I always felt it was essential for me to remind everyone who I was. *I* was the mom. Although it made logical sense, it frustrated me when all questions were addressed to Melissa and not me. But *I was* the mom! And *that was* my baby! During one appointment, the ultrasound technician assumed that I was Melissa's sister and inquired as to why Gregg was in the room. Before I could correct her and remark on how maybe she should have actually, like, read the chart, Melissa very quickly responded, "No, they are the parents." As I reflect on this now, I know it was just my own insecurities and nervousness surfacing, and I appreciate how patient everyone was with me.

We had no idea what pregnancy would be like; we only knew what infertility treatments were like. Above all, we had to learn how to rely on Melissa's judgment while she was pregnant. We met her wonderful kids and encouraged her to repeat this process and carry another perfect baby. Melissa was so warm, open, and inclusive with us at all appointments, and she was responsive every time I texted her. When we would schedule the next doctor's appointment, she always deferred to us first about dates that worked, since we were the ones commuting to the appointments. All these little things increased our confidence in her. Also, Melissa signed paperwork at the doctor's office, permitting the doctor to share all information with us at any time, which raised our comfort level. All that mattered was that the baby was growing healthy, and Melissa was healthy. After every appointment, we would take another breath and sigh of relief.

* * *

MELISSA'S PERSPECTIVE

All IVF pregnancies are considered high-risk. Many end in miscarriage or, even after a positive pregnancy test, the pregnancy turns out not to be viable for whatever reason. I also now know how common twins and their associated risks are when transferring two healthy embryos. We were all so very lucky, since, from our first ultrasound, we saw only one baby. Very early, Dr. B saw something that could have been the other embryo trying to implant, but it never did, so there was never a concern that we had twins.

One of the strongest memories for me was when Emily and Gregg were able to hear the heartbeat for the first time, which was one of many moments that validated my decision to become a surrogate. They were amazed, elated, and grateful. There were tears of happiness, hope, and disbelief. At another appointment very early on (around eight to ten weeks), we had an ultrasound where Emily and Gregg saw their little one move. I don't think either of them were prepared to see movement that early on. Gregg took video of the ultrasound and, after the ultrasound was finished, we all walked out to set up our next appointment. After figuring out a few dates and times, I turned around to confer with Gregg. He was leaning up against the wall, jaw to the floor, with tears in his eyes, watching that video. It was such a beautiful moment that I will never forget.

At around twelve weeks pregnant, we had our final appointment with our incredible reproductive endocrinologist (RE), Dr. B. Emily transformed it into a little party, bringing chocolate-covered strawberries and sparkling cider. This was a very special day for me, as my husband and children attended this appointment. It was so thoughtful for Emily and Gregg to involve my family as much as possible in everything we did. It was a great day and a fulfilling way to conclude that phase of the pregnancy.

As much as I loved our RE, I was very happy to begin seeing my own OB-GYN, Dr. N. He had been my doctor for both of my pregnancies, and I knew him well and was comfortable with him. Also, his office was only five minutes from my house, which was great for me, but now Emily and Gregg had to make the trip north in Los Angeles traffic to attend the appointments. Despite their lengthy drive, *nothing* was going to stop them from seeing their baby develop. They were committed to being at every appointment to see the progress.

Because I was so used to my doctor, I didn't even consider warning Emily and Gregg about how softly and quickly he spoke. During our very first appointment, Emily and Gregg both very slowly leaned in closer to hear what my doctor was saying. Emily eventually understood him pretty well, but so many times I could tell by the look on Gregg's face that he was totally lost!

Despite this, I believed that Emily and Gregg began to understand why I loved Dr. N so much. His laid-back demeanor was a calming presence, even in the delivery room. Dr. N had been a doctor for more than twenty-five years and had assisted intended parents and surrogates before, so he understood the dynamics of our pregnancy.

We also saw a perinatologist twice, shortly after being released to Dr. N. There is a test called a Nuchal Translucency (NT) test that is recommended by the surrogacy agency. Most regular OBs do not perform this test, so Dr. N recommended we go see Dr. S for it. Dr. S had a very high-tech and fancy ultrasound machine to be able to conduct the test. Ultimately, this test measures the fluid behind the back of the neck. If it is above a certain range, there is a chance for Down syndrome. This test can also check for a few other abnormalities. The NT test is typically used to decide if a couple should do an amniocentesis for further clarification of the baby's diagnosis. For us, the test results were good. And our next time back to Dr. S would be at around twenty-three weeks to have a full anatomical scan and fetal echo to make sure the heart was good. Happily, both ultrasounds came back perfect, and Dr. S gave the baby a clean bill of health!

Having Emily and Gregg at every appointment made the journey so much more real for me. As a surrogate, you have to be connected to the pregnancy and your body without becoming too attached to the baby, which is a fine line. Having them there every step of the way made it easier for me to concentrate on just myself and the pregnancy, not on the baby. I was able to direct my focus toward getting us to forty weeks—which I accomplished with ease. I know in many surrogacy relationships this isn't possible, but having that much involvement was perfect and worked for us.

* * *

7

The Pregnancy

"You have never really lived until you have done
something for someone who can never repay you."
—John Bunyan

EMILY'S PERSPECTIVE

Honestly, I never felt connected to the pregnancy or to the baby. My head knew what was happening, but my heart really didn't. I think I just subconsciously created a layer of protection around myself, and it took me until about three months after she was born to let that wall down. One example of how Gregg and I felt like outsiders was that, although Ava was kicking Melissa constantly, I only felt her kick once, and Gregg never felt a kick.

I mainly communicated with Melissa via text. We loved it when Melissa would notify us about what the baby was doing and loved whenever she sent us bump photos. She never complained to us if she wasn't feeling well. If she ever confessed that her feet were swollen or that she was tired, she immediately would dismiss it as "just normal pregnancy stuff." I always felt that she didn't want to complain to us but that she must have been revealing all these feelings to her husband. We assumed that he was the one rubbing her feet, helping with the kids, and so forth, so we grew to appreciate Kevin's role just as much as Melissa's. The attention was all on Melissa, but we recognized Kevin's sacrifice in carrying our baby for us, too.

I decided early on that I wanted us to do everything that typically would be done if we were the ones pregnant. We had a gender reveal party with our friends and family at our house, where we asked everyone to wear pink or blue to show us what they thought we were having. We performed the "reveal" to our friends by tying pink balloons to our dog Dixie's collar and then having her run down the stairs into the living room. It was important to us to be able to share this very special time in our lives.

Because of our love for travel, we even went on a "babymoon" to France. As I was not pregnant myself, I could drink wine, eat cheese, and walk everywhere. We felt like we deserved this dream trip because of everything we had been through for three years, and our time there together was special and memorable. However, a few days into our trip, we received an email from Melissa, and my heart sank—she knew we were traveling, and she would only contact us for something important. She informed us that she was bleeding and having some contractions and had been admitted to the hospital. Up to this point, the pregnancy had been totally uneventful, so we were really scared for Melissa and the baby. It figured that we would be helplessly on the other side of the world when this (our only) pregnancy concern occurred! Everything she wrote to us in the email showed us that she did exactly what she should have done by not just dismissing the bleeding and contractions as normal. We called Melissa to talk to her, and she felt so bad that this happened while we were on vacation. But, thankfully, everything was fine.

At seven months pregnant, my mom and I hosted a luncheon for the special women in Melissa's life and in mine. We held it at a restaurant near where Melissa lives, because the less she had to drive, the better. I felt the need to keep her in a protective bubble. Our desire was to celebrate Melissa, and also to provide an opportunity for the women in my life to meet Melissa and actually see the baby bump. We also wanted to show Melissa's friends and family who I was and the community that this baby was going to be so loved in and welcomed into. My mom even wrote a special poem to Melissa, which she shared at the luncheon on that special day and reads as follows:

Angels really do exist on earth
We finally have the proof
Because of you, Melissa
A baby will soon be under our family's roof

After three years of inseminations and IVF
Numerous procedures, disappointments, and tears
A miracle has actually happened
We can finally switch our gears

Your gift to our family is just priceless
Your generosity is beyond compare
You are filled with goodness and selfless love
These wonderful traits are so very rare

You have made Emily and Gregg so happy
Loving parents they can now be
You opened your amazing heart to us
And embraced us all with your surrogacy

All of our dreams for a baby
Can now come true
This has only happened
Because of you

One person can make such a difference
With one very generous act
Melissa, you are an inspiration to us all
I know this for a fact

Saying "thank you" just doesn't seem good enough
We are so deeply grateful to you
Happiness and good health is our wish
For you and your beautiful family too!

My friends and my mom's friends also threw me my
own baby shower, which included wine tasting—because,
well, I could drink! I felt I deserved to reap at least some
benefits from all the hell I went through with infertility,
and not being pregnant meant I could enjoy wine. I was
touched to have friends and family members host this

shower for me.

Up to this point, I had attended baby shower after baby shower, hosted many showers myself, and bought tons of baby gifts, all the while suffering with my own infertility and never knowing if I would be able to conceive or have a biological child. I always tried to retain the perspective that going to baby showers would give me good baby vibes, and I naturally wanted to celebrate my friends' happiness. But I'm not going to lie—this was incredibly hard for me, as baby showers can be rough, especially when some friends were now pregnant with baby number two while I was still trying for number one! So, when it was finally time for my own baby shower, I was overwhelmed.

During the pregnancy, no one knew that I was pregnant (obviously). I remember going to the market, seeing other pregnant women, and hearing people ask them, "What are you having? Is this your first?" This would make me sad, as no one questioned what I was having because I wasn't pregnant. However, I knew that people would present Melissa with these questions. I began to wonder how she would answer people, so one day I asked her. Melissa told me that she sometimes would respond, "It's not mine, I'm a surrogate," whereas other times she would just say, "It's a girl." This latter response made total sense to me because strangers might not agree with or understand the concept of surrogacy.

The final group I needed to inform about the pregnancy were those at my workplace, and I wasn't sure *how* to tell them. I was not physically pregnant and was a little worried about what some people might say or feel about surrogacy; I just didn't want to spark any office gossip. I decided to tell my boss at the start of the second trimester, which is the standard time for pregnant women to share the news. Although I could have waited a lot longer, I felt it was only right to share the news so that we could start putting plans in place for my department while I would be out on maternity leave. Thankfully, my boss, Alan, was really supportive of and happy for me. I then shared the news with my other colleagues, who had the same reaction.

During the next several months of work before the baby was born, my colleagues would ask me questions about surrogacy. They were mostly curious about who our surrogate was, and why a woman would want to do this for a total stranger. Like most perceptions about surrogates, they all assumed that she agreed to do it for the money. This is simply not true, at least for those surrogates who are properly psychologically screened and evaluated. I shared with my colleagues that surrogates are women who had loved being pregnant, and who had easily conceived their own children and loved being moms. Yes, money *was* a factor, but surrogates do not get paid nearly enough when you consider all of the physical and emotional risks they assume when being pregnant with someone else's baby. Just like with my own family and friends, I was always happy to discuss surrogacy and infertility with any of my colleagues. My colleagues even threw me a work baby shower!

At eight months pregnant, we did a maternity photoshoot with Melissa. Some beautiful photos were taken, as well as lots of "bump pics." Gregg and I also spent this time registering for baby items. We set up our baby's room with a crib, glider, and dresser and washed all her baby clothes to have them ready for her.

A few weeks before the baby was due, I called the hospital to make sure they had our legal paperwork, specifically the court documents that declared Gregg and me as the legal parents. I was glad I had the forethought to check on this, as, for whatever reason, they did not. So, I immediately contacted our lawyer's office, which replied that they had already certified mailed it to the hospital, but that they would do it again. I also verified that Melissa was registered with the hospital and had a copy of the court documents with her in her hospital bag in case she should arrive at the hospital before we did. The last detail involving the hospital was to rent a breast pump for Melissa, since she had offered to pump breast milk for us for the first few weeks.

We also toured the hospital. Melissa already knew it well, having given birth there for her two kids, but we wanted to do the tour together. Gregg, Melissa, and I were the only "threesome" placed in a group consisting of two-partner relationships. To alleviate any awkwardness about the situation, I remember lightheartedly joking that maybe people thought we were polygamists and that Gregg had two wives, one of whom was pregnant!

As much as possible, Gregg and I wanted to enjoy the many aspects of having a baby. For us, participating in all of these expected activities helped us to feel a bit more connected to the fact that we were having a baby.

* * *

MELISSA'S PERSPECTIVE

Overall, the pregnancy was easy and uneventful, which is exactly what you want. The only issue was when I started spotting and having minor contractions at around twenty-three weeks, naturally the one time when Emily and Gregg were out of the country. The second my doctor's office opened, I gave them a call and was told to head to the hospital for monitoring.

As a surrogate, you have this heightened sense of responsibility because people who have been through so much are counting on you. Not that I didn't feel a sense of responsibility when I was pregnant with my own children—of course I did. It is just a completely different feeling when you are carrying someone else's child. I was nervous and wracking my brain for something I could have done to cause this because I thought for sure that Emily and Gregg would ask me that. Although I knew they would want to be aware of any complications, I didn't want to ruin their vacation with what was likely unnecessary worry, so I didn't contact them right away.

I was hooked up to the monitors, and my doctor ordered an internal and external ultrasound to find the source of the bleeding. They found nothing, and the only contractions the monitor was picking up were minor. The nurses made me drink more water, and it all went away—no more spotting or contractions. My doctor determined that I may have been slightly dehydrated, which would have caused the contractions, and the spotting could have been caused by anything. When you are pregnant, there is extra blood flow to your uterus, and sometimes a capillary can burst from something as simple as a sneeze or a cough. The most important thing was that the baby's heartbeat was great the whole time, and she was moving, so I knew that she was fine.

The next day, I emailed my counselor at the agency to inform her of what had happened at the hospital. She was *not* happy, to say the least! She reminded me that she needed to be made aware of anything like this immediately, no matter how unimportant I might feel it was. And if I couldn't talk, I needed to have my husband call. She then instructed me to email Emily and Gregg right away to let them know. She understood my desire not to disrupt their vacation, but not letting them know could destroy the trust that we had all worked so hard to build. So, I carefully drafted a detailed email to Emily, making sure she knew everything that had happened, what my doctor did, what the hospital did, and what the outcome was.

Although part of me feared that Emily and Gregg would be upset with me, it was just the opposite—they were grateful, and they were worried about how I was faring. The first sentence in their response focused on gratitude that I was so on top of it and had sought help at the first possible sign of trouble. The second sentence was, "How are you feeling? Is everything with you okay?" It was reassuring to know that they still trusted me and cared for me, too. I apologized profusely for having waited two days to tell them anything, but they were understanding of my reasons for that as well.

After that small hiccup, it was smooth sailing—other than the unbelievable heartburn, not being able to sleep for longer than a few minutes at a time because of the incredible pain in my hips, and being super tired. But that, for me, was all a normal part of pregnancy. Emily and Gregg continued to be at every appointment and checked on me and how I was feeling just about every day, which was sweet.

My entire family and my friends were all incredibly supportive throughout the pregnancy, but it didn't start off that way. When I first told my parents about being a surrogate, my mom cried and said I was giving away her grandchild. My dad said, "Wow, are you that hard up for money?" Once the ball got rolling on things and I was able to have a conversation with my parents face-to-face, they were able to understand. Neither of them really had any idea what gestational surrogacy was, so when that was clarified, they were behind me 100 percent. My mom even came to a few doctor's appointments to see the baby. My close friends cried and thought it was an incredible gift, and they were so proud of me. I had a few acquaintances who would make comments like, "Oh, I couldn't do that, I wouldn't be able to give up the baby," and I would just smile and nod because I knew that these people didn't really understand it.

The most important people to hear the news of my plan to be a surrogate were my children. I didn't want to tell them anything too soon in case something happened, as I didn't want to confuse them. So, I told them a little later in the first trimester. They were so great because, at their ages, they didn't really know that carrying someone else's baby was out of the ordinary. I told them that I had a baby in my tummy, but that it was Emily and Gregg's baby, and they just accepted it and went on about their day. My son was five at the time, and he really got it. Once I started showing and we started getting the related questions, he was always quick to tell the person, "That's not our baby," which led to some unnecessary and sometimes awkward conversations with strangers. But I knew that he understood, and that was what was most important to me.

Kevin was the biggest support to me by far. He never really felt connected to the baby or the pregnancy. I think at times, it was hard for him to figure out his place in this whole process. Whenever the baby would kick, he didn't want to feel it, and he only came to a few appointments. But he always stayed connected to me and my needs, which was all I ever needed.

The support from Emily and Gregg was incredible. As I mentioned before, they were at every appointment, and they would text every day to see how I was feeling. But above that, they were also incredibly generous. They would give me little gifts here and there and always ask me if I needed anything. Emily even threw me a bit of a shower; we called it a "celebration of Melissa." She invited my friends and family and her closest friends and family so we could all meet. It was an incredible day. I felt so special and so spoiled!

* * *

8

Labor and Delivery

*"How your baby came into this world is far less
important than the fact that she's here."*
—Unknown

EMILY'S PERSPECTIVE

Our due date was February 13, my mom's birthday. On February 9, Melissa, Kevin, Gregg, and I went to lunch together in Los Angeles at a restaurant that offers a "special" salad dressing that supposedly helps induce labor. It was another "pregnancy thing" to do, and Melissa and Kevin were all for it. I think Kevin was the most supportive, as he was ready for Melissa to not be pregnant anymore, and we didn't blame him!

We were eating when Melissa's phone rang. It was Dr. N, who was calling to tell Melissa that he had to head out of town, so he might not be there when she delivered. Because we all wanted him to deliver the baby, we decided to have the baby the next day, before he left town. This meant that Melissa would need to be induced on a significant date in my life, as I will explain shortly.

On February 9, Gregg and I went to a happy hour to cheers our final night as a couple (plus our doggy Dixie) and cheers to the next chapter of our lives starting the following day. Then, on February 10, Gregg and I drove to the hospital to have a baby! We got there and waited a little bit for Melissa and Kevin to arrive. We weren't sure where they were, and we were concerned because Melissa had always been on time to every appointment. But soon, Melissa and Kevin arrived, and everything began. It turned out that Melissa was already in labor. So, the nurses believed that with the induction, the baby would be born by midday or early afternoon. We were thrilled!

Well, in reality, it ended up being a *long* day. Thankfully, the nurses made the wait easier and were so sweet with Melissa and us. Although we had been told that Dr. N was going to come in around noon to check on Melissa, we only saw him in the hallway. We really wanted to have the doctor in the room, but the nurses assured us that they were updating him on the phone throughout the day. Gregg and I routinely checked in with the nursing station. We knew that we had to balance not being annoying to the nurses and not overwhelming Melissa, but we needed a better feel of what was going on. My mom and Melissa's parents were in the waiting room at the hospital all day; we would either let them come in the room or visit with them in the waiting area to keep them updated as well.

It was now the afternoon, and Melissa had remained dilated the same amount with no progress. I started to get antsy and anxious, and it became harder and harder to keep myself in check so as not to stress Melissa out. It was then nighttime, we were all tired and emotional, and Melissa's contractions were growing more and more intense. Gregg and I eventually left the room for a little while, both to give Melissa some space and to get some fresh air. After we walked out, we left a message for Dr. N to determine exactly when he would be coming, but it turned out that he was already in the hospital when we called. He came in and checked on Melissa and revealed that he had previously instructed the nurses to turn Melissa on her side because the baby was slanted. Well, that never happened. Now we knew why labor was taking far longer than we were told it would. So, Melissa was turned on her side, her water broke, and it was finally time to push!

My mom was in the room with Melissa when the doctor came in, whereas Gregg and I were laying down in one of the waiting rooms. My mom came running in and told us, "It's time!" Gregg and I saw Melissa's mom and dad in the waiting area, gave them a big hug, and ran to Melissa. The time was now around 11:40 p.m. Our initial plan for the birth was that Gregg would stand at Melissa's shoulder to give her some privacy, and I would stand anywhere I wanted. When we came into the room, Kevin explained that they had decided that Gregg was welcome to stand anywhere he wanted to see his baby be born. Kevin told Gregg that he had been able to see his two children born and wanted that same opportunity for Gregg. Despite this thoughtful offer, Gregg ultimately ended up standing facing me, taking photos and video of me during the birth.

At midnight, I saw the baby's head of dark hair crowning. Watching my baby be born was the most surreal moment of my life. I felt warm and tingly all over, and I numbly tried to stay present as best I could. Melissa was a champ, and Dr. N was calm and collected. Kevin lovingly held Melissa's hand and knee, supporting her. Gregg and I were already starting to cry, as we knew we were minutes away from meeting our daughter. After three hard years, we were about to become parents. And at 12:28 a.m. on February 11, Ava Giselle Field was born. Dr. N let me cut the cord; I was so shaky, but I cut the cord. Dr. N. also had Gregg do a cut of the cord. FINALLY, I WAS A MOM!

While Melissa was recovering from the delivery, I brought snacks and drinks for her and Kevin. I was still bothered by the fact that the hospital might not understand that we were the parents, so I brought a big tub of popcorn for the nurses with a note on it that said, "Thank you for taking such good care of our surrogate and baby." It was just my way of dealing with the insecurities I had regarding making sure people knew that the baby was ours.

The day before Ava's birth, February 10, had marked the ten-year anniversary of my father's death. My dad tragically and unexpectedly died at the age of fifty-three, when I was twenty-three years old. He was on his way home from a business trip, and the small private plane he was on crashed shortly before landing, with no survivors. When my friends and family learned that Ava's due date was February 13, everyone believed that she was going to be born a few days earlier. And, while in the hospital on February 10, we definitely thought that it was going to happen then. But my dad apparently wanted Ava to have her own day—a day that was filled with complete joy and no grief. I truly believe this. All throughout my infertility treatments and then through surrogacy, Dr. B strongly felt that my dad was part of it, as did I. Dr. B took care of everything medically and scientifically, Melissa took care of everything physically, and my dad took care of everything spiritually. It truly does make you wonder.

* * *

MELISSA'S PERSPECTIVE

In terms of the pregnancy and delivery, the one thing I was certain I wanted to stay away from was an induction. I was induced with my son, which made it a very long labor and delivery since my little guy just didn't want to come out yet. Because Emily and Gregg lived relatively close by, there was no reason to schedule anything, although I was aware that some surrogates and intended parents (a.k.a. Emily and Gregg, the mom and dad) have inductions to ensure that the couple is there for the delivery. But I made my preference clear from the start, and my doctor said that would not be a problem, assuming that I didn't go past my due date. The week before my February 13 due date, I had dilated a few centimeters, Ava had dropped, and my cervix had thinned out. I had also started to feel contractions that would grow strong, then die down—all familiar signs that I was gearing up for labor.

On Monday, February 9, Emily, Gregg, Kevin, and I decided to meet for lunch. I had heard of a place called the Caioti Café that had a famous labor-inducing salad. I had actually been there when I was pregnant with my daughter, and the salad had given me some major contractions afterward. (I didn't end up going into labor until three days later, but I believe that the contractions the salad caused were what helped get me there.) The dressing they use on the salad has many ingredients in it that are known to be natural labor inducers. So, we all thought it would be fun to meet there, especially since it was about halfway between our homes. We had a lovely lunch. Gregg even bought me an extra container of the salad dressing to take home to help things move along.

Right at the end of the meal, my phone rang, and it was my doctor. He told me that he unexpectedly had to go out of town later that week, from February 12–16. Because there was a strong possibility that I would go into labor while he was gone, he wanted to give me the option to be induced the next day to ensure that he would be there for my delivery. While I really did not want to be induced again, I could not imagine anyone else delivering this baby. Dr. N had been my doctor for every appointment up until this point; in addition, our situation was special and different, and Dr. N knew us and had approved of all of us being in the delivery room. The thought of him not being there made me uneasy, but I remembered that there were other people involved in this decision as well.

I hung up the phone, walked back into the restaurant, and said, "Well, this dressing might have really worked!" I explained the situation to Emily, Gregg, and Kevin, and while all three of them ultimately put the decision on me, we were all on the same page: Dr. N *had* to be there. We could not risk me going into labor while he was out of town, so we called him back and notified him that we were opting for the induction the next morning, at 8:00 a.m.

On the way to the hospital, Kevin and I dropped off our kids with my in-laws and made a quick stop at Starbucks. We thus arrived closer to 8:30 a.m., and, to my surprise, Emily and Gregg were already there. I felt guilty because here I was, waltzing in with Starbucks, and they had been there eagerly waiting for me. Despite the delay, I was quickly all hooked up to the monitors, and the nurses informed me that I was already having contractions strong enough to be picked up by the monitors, so I was already in the beginning stages of labor. This thankfully indicated that the induction would not be as long and as difficult as it had been with my son, because back then, my body had not been ready yet. I was now hopeful that this would be an easier experience.

Somewhere around 9:00 a.m., we began the Pitocin drip. Everything was great for the next several hours while we waited for the Pitocin to gear up and really start working its magic; my contractions were light and manageable. All four of us were in the room together, chatting and having a great time. After a while, we closed the blinds and were resting or reading. Well, I was resting—everyone else was reading. The nurses would check on me periodically, and I was dilating slowly but surely. Everything was on track.

At some point later in the afternoon, Emily and Gregg moved to the waiting room, along with Emily's mom and my parents. My parents had arrived in the late afternoon because they wanted to be there for me in case I needed emotional support. We were all one big happy family at this point, so everyone was welcome. They gave me my privacy for a while, and then they would cycle in to say *hi*. I think everyone was respecting the fact that, as the contractions were stepping up, I was uncomfortable and didn't want everyone staring at me. I never had to say anything; they just gave me space, which was sweet and intuitive.

In the early evening, things stalled a bit. My contractions were getting much stronger, but they weren't doing much to get Ava down to dilate my cervix. I asked if we could possibly break my water to get things going, but the nurse determined that the baby was too high, which could risk infection. We even tried an enema as well, thinking that might help, but it did nothing to progress things. They did a great job trying to hide it from me, but I could tell that Emily and Gregg were getting anxious and confused. They could not understand why we hadn't seen Dr. N, but they just weren't familiar with hospital protocol. The doctor doesn't come in until the end, to deliver; instead, the nurses remain in touch with him every hour, giving him updates until he is needed for the actual delivery.

I think Emily and Gregg somehow sensed that the nurses were missing something, so they called Dr. N's office to see if he could come in. Luckily, he is a very sweet man, so he agreed and came in to check on me. He politely asked why I was laying on my back. I looked at him, confused, and he said he had told the nurse to lay me on my right side because, based on what she was telling him, he knew Ava was coming down crooked and not hitting my cervix, which was why I wasn't dilating. He checked and, sure enough, that was the case. He had me lay on my right side, and then he left to check on his other patients.

By the time Dr. N came back, Ava had dropped low enough to be able to break my water. That was painful and uncomfortable, but it really got things moving! My contractions hit hard at that point, and I was begging for the epidural. Luckily, the anesthesiologist was able to get there quickly and administer it. After that, I was comfortable and relaxed and happy that things were progressing without pain. Dr. N left again and said that he would be back when I was ten centimeters. Everyone began to cycle through again to see me, but it was getting late, and everyone was tired. Emily and Gregg fell asleep in the lobby while my parents read and watched television. Kevin was asleep next to my bed, and Lois, Emily's mom, was sitting next to me, keeping me company. Around 11:00 p.m., the nurse checked me, and I was now at ten centimeters. It was go time! I will never forget Lois's face when she went running out in excitement to tell Emily and Gregg. Shortly after, Emily and Gregg rushed in, and they were so emotional.

The nurses set up the room while we waited for Dr. N to arrive, and everyone was shuffled around. Our original birth plan was to have Gregg behind my head and Emily and Kevin on either side of me. But the way the room was set up with the monitors, lights, and people, there was just too much stuff next to, around, and behind me, though there was ample room in front of me. Without saying a word, Kevin and I looked at each other and nodded. He went over and told everyone not to worry about where they were standing or what they said. At this point, all that mattered was seeing that beautiful girl be born; I felt, in that moment, that Emily and Gregg needed to be the first two to see her. I still have the unforgettable image in my head of them hugging and crying with their foreheads touching, saying, "This is it!" At around 11:30 p.m., it was time to push.

Now is a good time to mention the significance of February 10, my induction day. Emily's father had died on February 10 years earlier, so this day had always been filled with a lot of sadness for her family. When Dr. N called to ask about the induction, we all knew that would likely mean that Ava would be born on the anniversary of her grandfather's death. I immediately asked Emily at the restaurant how she felt about this. Would there forever be this cloud over Ava's birthday so that no one could truly enjoy it? Or would it completely morph and change the meaning of the day for them into something happy and positive? Ava would, after all, be named in honor of her grandfather. Emily quickly had an answer—she knew it was a sign, and she believed that Ava being born on the anniversary would surround the day with love and happiness rather than grief and sorrow.

Well, apparently Ava and her grandfather had a *different* idea. With labor being induced at 9:00 a.m., while I was already having contractions, we never considered that this labor was going to last as long as it did. And no one thought that I would need to push for forty-five minutes, either, since Ava had dropped and this was my third delivery. But all those assumptions quickly went out the window as we blew past midnight and into a new day.

Ava came shortly after midnight on February 11. She was perfect and healthy, and her parents were overjoyed. That is another picture in my head that I will never forget: the moment they saw their daughter for the first time, which made everything worth it. I later asked Emily how she felt about Ava being born later than we had intended, and I learned that Emily and her mom believed that her father had planned it that way. He wanted Ava to have her own day, all to herself, and that is exactly what she got. Now they would be able to grieve one day and then turn around and immediately have the joy of celebrating a momentous occasion the next. It was perfect.

EXPERIENCING SURROGACY

* * *

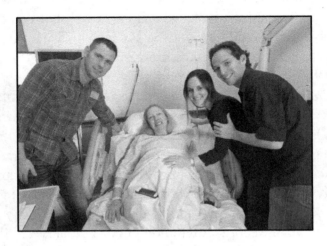

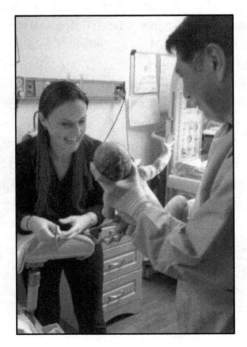

Labor and Delivery

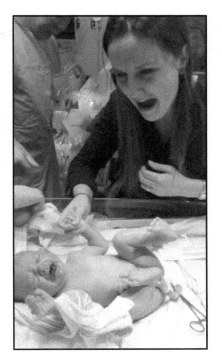

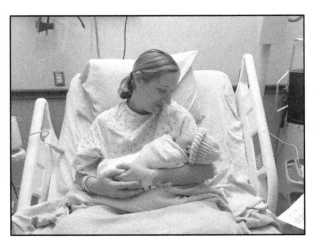

9

Postdelivery in the Hospital

"I'm proud of many things in my life, but nothing beats being a surrogate."
—Sacredsurrogacy.com

EMILY'S PERSPECTIVE

Ava went straight to the nurse, who wrapped her and put her on the warm bassinet. We were in the delivery room for about five to ten minutes after the baby was born before she was wheeled to another room, and we followed. It was a blur to us. I felt weird leaving Melissa so soon, but I knew that we would visit together while in the hospital.

The hospital staff were accommodating to our situation and told us that they were going to try hard to get us our own room. If for some reason we could not get our own room, then the plan was for Melissa, the baby, and me to share a room, and Gregg would stay in a hotel nearby. We were really close at the time of the birth, but I know that all of us were hoping for separate rooms. Melissa needed to recover, and Gregg and I wanted to share our first night as a family of three. We were lucky, and there was a room available for us.

The nurse weighed and measured Ava at a perfect seven pounds, eleven ounces. Ava and I then did skin-to-skin contact, and I noticed that her face and head were round and perfect. I kept looking at her tiny fingers and toes and could not stop kissing her head. Gregg then did skin-to-skin. He was holding Ava, crying. Although so much about this time remains a blur to me, I have a vivid picture in my head of Gregg's eyes closed, tears flowing, holding Ava against his chest. We had finally made my husband a dad!

Gregg then went to the waiting room to get my mom, who came in and held Ava. My mom could not believe how beautiful and precious her granddaughter was. Gregg and I then enjoyed our first night together as new parents. I was focused on the baby, but I was thinking of Melissa and how she was doing and recovering. I texted her a bunch of photos because Kevin told us that she was sleeping while we were up doing diapers.

Once Melissa was awake, we invited her and Kevin to come into our room to meet Ava and hold her. Later in the day, Melissa, Kevin, and Melissa's mom came in to give Ava her first bath. When Melissa was talking, Ava would turn her head toward her, as she recognized her voice. Since I had been told to expect this, it did not bother me at all; in fact, I felt comforted that Ava knew the amazing woman who brought her to me.

My mom visited with us, and so did my best friend. We were in the hospital for a day and a half and left when

Melissa was dismissed. As we were getting ready to leave the hospital, a hospital volunteer came into our room with a wheelchair—for me. I reminded her that I did not give birth myself so would be able to walk out. But because I was the mom and hospital policy says that moms must be wheeled out to their cars, I got in while Gregg carried Ava out in the car seat. We totally laughed about this, and I enjoyed being wheeled out to our car! As soon as we got home, I texted Melissa to let her know that we were home safe and sound.

* * *

MELISSA'S PERSPECTIVE

Right after delivery, they cleaned up Ava in the delivery room with Emily and Gregg watching over her lovingly. Obviously, the nurses and other hospital staff knew our situation and were very understanding and generous. Apparently, my hospital had done several surrogacy deliveries, so this was nothing new. They had promised us that we could all have our own postpartum room—*if* they had the space. That was one of those things that cannot be predicted, and if they didn't have a spare room, we would be forced to share. As much as I loved them all, I was hoping we could have our own rooms. I was exhausted and wanted my own space to rest and heal. In addition, they had just welcomed a newborn, and I wanted them to have their own space to develop that bond as a family of three.

While I had been laboring the night before, my nurse told me that their labor and delivery rooms were currently full. That wasn't a good sign, because all of those women would need a postpartum room eventually. Well, at some point in the evening, about half of those women were sent home due to not being in active labor. Maybe not so lucky for them, but super lucky for us! Once the nurses had done all their assessments on Ava, Emily and Gregg took her to their own room to start bonding. Seeing the three of them walk out of the room, thanking me profusely, was another picture-perfect moment that I will never forget. They were in heaven.

After I was all cleaned up, the nurse brought my parents in. I honestly had assumed they had gone home at some point, since it was now after 1:00 a.m. But I should have known better. My mother needed to see me to know I was okay before she could go home and rest. At the moment they walked in, I felt my second wind and was happy and giddy—mostly from the fact that I had given Emily and Gregg an amazing gift, but also because I was eating for the first time in more than thirty hours!

When my parents left, I finished my sandwich, and then the fatigue set in: I needed to sleep. I was able to nap for a bit in the labor room while I waited for the hospital to get my postpartum room ready. At 5:00 a.m., I was moved to my room. Kevin never left my side; he even came and slept in the postpartum room with me. The great thing about postdelivery as a surrogate is that the nurses leave you alone. Aside from assistants coming in periodically to take vitals, unless I called someone, they stayed away. That was the best sleep I have ever had in a hospital, by far.

Dr. N came in to check on me around 9:00 a.m. He decided that everything looked good and that, although I was supposed to be in the hospital for twenty-four hours after delivery, because I gave birth at just after midnight, he could clear me to go home that evening. At that point, I was still numb from the epidural and so exhausted that I couldn't imagine going home and jumping back into normal life as a mom of two young children. I asked if it would be alright to stay the night and get released the next morning. Without hesitation, Dr. N said absolutely. He left, and I settled back in to get more sleep.

Around 11:00 a.m., I started to receive texts from Emily, asking if I wanted to come and meet Ava. Of course I did! But the epidural had just worn off, and I was still very wobbly on my feet. It made me nervous to get up and walk the few steps to my bathroom, let alone to the other side of the maternity ward. When I let them know this, their response was, "No problem! We will bring her to you!" If I weren't still so exhausted, I think that moment would have been much more emotional for me. But Ava was perfect and beautiful, and I could not believe that I was holding her and that she was here. Emily and Gregg were both very emotional seeing me hold her, which I thought was so sweet.

Later in the day, Emily and Gregg invited us down to watch Ava have her first bath. My mom had come back to the hospital to see me and meet Ava, so she came, too. I loved that they were not only open but eager to share these special firsts with my family. It was awesome to all be in there, laughing and passing Ava around. Surrounded by so much love and gratitude, my heart was full.

The next morning, we were all released at the same time. Kevin and I went to Emily, Gregg, and Ava's room one last time to hold Ava and say goodbye. Saying goodbye was easy because I knew I would be seeing them relatively often. I know so many surrogates who have a hard time with that goodbye because their intended parents are leaving to go back home, which could be on the other side of the world. Not knowing when or if you are going to see them all again makes those goodbyes harder. I was so lucky that my intended parents lived locally.

I was glad that I had decided to stay the extra night to get the extra care and rest, but at this point, I wanted nothing more than my home, my kids, and my own bed. I was ready to return to my life before surrogacy. Not that I wanted to forget surrogacy or leave it behind, but it had been a big focal point of my life for the past year, and now I was ready and excited to focus solely on my own family again.

Gregg and Emily had asked me if I would pump breastmilk for Ava. I was torn at first: I knew it was the best thing for her and for me (pumping helps your uterus contract and go back down), but as I mentioned, I was ready for things to go back to normal. Having to pump every three to four hours to build up a supply sounded like, well, taking care of a newborn again. Ultimately, I knew what the right thing to do was for all involved, so I pumped for five weeks. At times it was difficult having to wake up in the middle of the night or take all my pump supplies everywhere I went, but I would not change it for the world. I truly felt like it was an extension of caring for Ava as I had for those precious nine months.

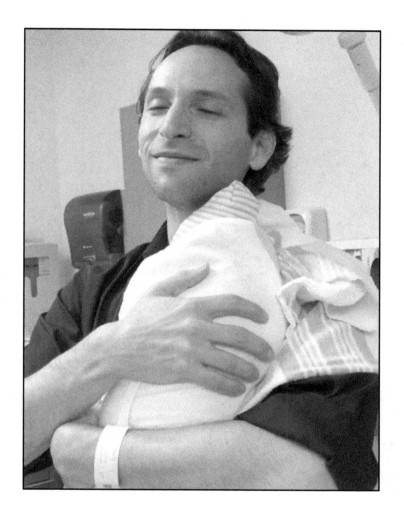

10

Our Relationship with Each Other

"It takes a village to raise a child, and, sometimes, it takes a village to have a child."
—Fertilityconsultants.ca

EMILY'S PERSPECTIVE

When we first started with surrogacy, Gregg looked at it as more of a business relationship. I did, too, but I was open to the possibility of a relationship that would last well after the birth. I wanted Ava to know her birth story and all of the people who created her. Melissa was nice, caring, and loving, which helped me be able to trust her. Trust is the foundation of any great relationship.

Throughout the pregnancy, a real relationship between us formed. I genuinely grew to love Melissa, Kevin, and their kids and parents. Our contract stated that our only requirement in a postdelivery relationship was to send Melissa a few pictures a year for the first few years. There was zero pressure on us to have a relationship. However, a relationship just somehow formed, and I'm so happy that it did.

Melissa and her family come to Ava's birthday parties, and we go to their kids' birthday parties. Melissa and her family were also part of Ava's baby naming ceremony. We asked Melissa to carry Ava into the room and hand her to me. We felt that this was a very symbolic way to begin our baby naming, where we would bless our daughter in front of our community of friends and family. We text frequently, and we get together a few times per year. After every doctor checkup appointment that Ava has, I send Melissa Ava's stats of her height, weight, and so forth. Melissa always responds with excitement. It truly is like sharing news about my daughter with a family member.

We refer to Melissa as "Auntie Melissa" and have photos of Melissa and her family in our home and in Ava's room. We point to the pictures, and Ava can name everyone in them. We also point to pictures of Melissa pregnant and ask Ava, "Who is in that tummy?" To which she responds, "Me!" We are proud of and thankful for Ava's birth story, and we will share every aspect of it with her.

* * *

MELISSA'S PERSPECTIVE

When I decided to become a surrogate, I thought that I would be able to give the greatest gift to a family, and that, in itself, would be pretty amazing. I never expected to gain so much for myself out of this experience. Not only did surrogacy change my life, but Emily and Gregg changed my life, too. I love the way they look at life and embrace adversity. Many couples who struggle with infertility shy away from the topic and suffer in silence. Not Emily and Gregg. They have been outspoken about their troubles in the hope of helping others who suffer from the same issues. I have learned so much from them on how to give back and turn something negative into a positive. I only hope that I can live my life with half as much courage and generosity as they do. I feel like my kids are and will continue to be more compassionate human beings by witnessing this journey as well.

We all entered into this as purely a business relationship. We had never met before, and we were joined together by an agency and a contract. It was never a requirement to have postdelivery contact. Emily and Gregg could have taken Ava home and sent me pictures a couple of times a year, and that would have been fine. This is what most surrogates get after their journey is over, and what all surrogates prepare themselves for. I never expected to discover lifelong friends out of this experience.

It just so happened that Emily, Gregg, Kevin, and I really like each other and enjoy each other's company. We have similar ideologies, and we have had amazing conversations about everything. Our relationship is not based around surrogacy or even Ava at this point. The four of us will go out to dinner without Ava or the kids. We are friends now, which is one of the best gifts I could have ever been given from this experience. Our families are intertwined forever. My kids know Emily, Gregg, and Ava very well, and Ava calls us "Aunt Melissa" and "Uncle Kevin." My parents are invited to Ava's birthdays. My loving Italian grandmother always believed that you make your family by whom you choose to love and be a part of your life. And the Fields and Dubins are family.

* * *

Afterword

Where We Are Now

"When you stand and share your story in an empowering way, your story will heal you and your story will heal somebody else."
—Iyanla Vanzant

EMILY AND HER HUSBAND GREGG started Field Fertility, a legal and consulting business that is a branch of Gregg's existing law practice. Emily runs the business, marketing, operations, and client relations, and Gregg is the lawyer and represents the clients, surrogates, egg donors, and/or intended parents. Ava is now in preschool.

Melissa works for a surrogacy agency, Center for Surrogate Parenting—the same agency that brought Melissa and Emily together. She is a surrogate coordinator and supports surrogates on their journeys. Melissa is now a surrogate again, for another couple.

We hope you have enjoyed reading about our journey from each of our perspectives and hope it provides you some ways to enhance your or someone else's experience. If you have any questions, please feel free to contact

Emily at emily@fieldfertility.com. You can also check out the surrogacy-related resources at www.fieldfertility.com. And please be sure to "Like" Field Fertility on Facebook and Instagram, at www.facebook.com/fieldfertility and www.instagram.com/fieldfertility.

From the Publisher

Thank You from the Publisher

Van Rye Publishing, LLC ("VRP") sincerely thanks you for your interest in and purchase of this book.

If you enjoyed this book or found it useful, VRP hopes you will please consider taking a moment to support the author and get word out to other readers like you by leaving a rating or review of the book at its product page at your favorite online book retailer. You can do so at Amazon by visiting the book's product page, scrolling down to the section labeled "Review This Product," and clicking on the button labeled "Write a Customer Review."

Thank you!

Resources from the Publisher

Van Rye Publishing, LLC ("VRP") offers the following resources to writers and to readers.

For *writers* who enjoyed this book or found it useful, please consider having VRP edit, format, or fully publish your own book manuscript. You can find out more and contact the publisher directly by visiting VRP's website:

From the Publisher

www.vanryepublishing.com.

For *readers* who enjoyed this book or found it useful, please consider signing up to have VRP notify you when books like this one are available at a limited-time discounted price, some as low as $0.99. You can sign up to receive such notifications by visiting the following web address: http://eepurl.com/cERow9.

For *anyone* who enjoyed this book or found it useful, if you have not already done so, VRP hopes you will please again consider leaving a customer rating or review of this book at its product page at your favorite online book retailer. These ratings and reviews are themselves extremely valuable resources for writers and for readers like you.

Thank you again!

Appendix A

Tips for Intended Parents

EMILY'S TIPS

Choosing Your Surrogacy Agency

If you are like my husband, Gregg, and I were, you are not sure how to go about finding a surrogacy agency to work with. Our fertility doctor recommended an agency to us, but we also wanted to interview a few others. In total, we interviewed three different agencies. I think interviewing three agencies is the right amount. We ended up learning a lot about surrogacy from these interviews and were ultimately able to make our decision on which agency was right for us because we spent time with each agency. We also got a feel for each agency's responsiveness to our emails and calls, which was very important to us. (I put together an agency questionnaire for you to give you an idea of the types of questions to ask. You can get it for free at www.fieldfertility.com.)

I recommend that you ask each agency the same several questions so that you can evaluate them similarly.

Most important, in my opinion, is how each agency recruits and screens its surrogates. Agencies tend to do this differently. Some agencies totally prescreen a surrogate prior to you being introduced to her, and some agency's surrogates are only partially screened and then completely screened after you meet. For example, we learned that some agencies psychologically screen a surrogate before you are introduced to her, and some do this after you are introduced to her. This difference is mainly based on how the agency covers the costs for these screenings. So, definitely ask each agency to thoroughly explain its process for recruiting and screening surrogates.

Also, make sure to ask what screening is done on a surrogate's husband/partner. Your surrogate, and her husband or partner if she has one, will undergo various screenings such as psychological screenings and assessments, criminal background checks, a financial check to make sure they are not on government assistance, medical screenings, and more. Some agencies do a house visit to the surrogate's home, and some agencies do not do this. Some offer support groups to their surrogates during the pregnancy, and some offer one on one counseling to the surrogates.

Our agency shared with us how many steps a surrogate candidate needs to go through before she even gets to a next step in the process of becoming a surrogate. For example, a surrogate candidate needs to submit an online application and needs to get her medical records and scan and email them in. This helps show how responsive and on it she is. Our agency told us that many surrogate candidates could not even do this, so they would get ruled out immediately.

Our agency also shared with us that, if a surrogate candidate asked about money in her first three questions, she was also ruled out immediately. Hearing this made us feel really good because our agency was clearly looking for surrogates who wanted to be a surrogate for more than just the money, and that really stands out in my mind. We also asked our agency if we could speak with a few of their former intended parent clients. Hearing that we could further reassured us that we were choosing the right agency to help us on our emotional, expensive journey to our baby.

You also want to feel a connection with whoever will be your main contact at your agency. Each agency is different. The agency's owner might be your main contact, or a case manager might be your main contact. Our main contact was an agency case manager, and we could go to her for anything. We felt such a warmth from her, like she wanted us to have a baby just as much as we did; it was more than just a job for her. We even invited her to attend our daughter's baby naming ceremony, which she did!

The role of your agency during your surrogacy is to help make sure your relationship with your surrogate remains strong; to help make sure that you, the intended parents, feel supported and educated about the process ahead; to coordinate all logistics for you; and more. Rely on your agency and the expertise of its staff. You are paying them a lot of money to help you! More so, for any questions, concerns, etc. you have, go to your agency first before going to your surrogate. You do not want to unintentionally say something to your surrogate that could hurt your relationship in any way. So, your best bet as an intended parent is to talk to your agency first.

And for those who do not use an agency to find your surrogate—and have a friend or family member who is your surrogate, or even a woman who you found in a surrogacy chat group online—you can still take the information from the tips in this appendix and apply them to your specific situation.

Choosing Your Surrogate

When we started to interview surrogacy agencies, they all asked us what we were looking for in our surrogate. At that time, we were not totally sure how to answer that question. So, in hopes of helping you, the following is a list of things you might want to think about in identifying your ideal surrogate.

- Where does she live? This is important for two reasons. First, surrogacy laws are different in every state. You can do a simple Google search to learn the surrogacy laws in the US and around the world. Second, how involved do you want to be in the pregnancy? Based on your answer to this, proximity might or might not be important. For example, do you want to attend every doctor's appointment? Or are you, instead, okay Skyping or FaceTiming into the appointments and attending only the major appointments in person? Based on your answer to such questions, maybe you are okay with your surrogate being a longer drive or plane ride away. But what about for the birth? If you live farther away from her, then you may need to stay in a hotel close to where she will be delivering as you get closer to the due date, and you will need to stay there until a pediatrician approves you to drive or fly home with your baby.

- Is she single or is she partnered/married? If she's single, what's her immediate support system like? Who makes up this support system? If she's married or in a committed relationship, what is her husband or partner like? How does he/she feel about surrogacy? It's a family decision for a surrogate to embark on surrogacy, as the surrogacy greatly impacts her immediate support system and family.

- How old are her kids? What if she has a toddler who requires her to carry him/her a lot and your surrogate is put on bed rest or restrictions? What support does she have to help with her kid(s)?

- What are your surrogate's, and her partner's/spouse's, beliefs on termination and reduction? Most important, are they in complete and total agreement and alignment with your own beliefs and wants on termination and reduction? This is a critical factor in finding your ideal surrogate.

- Who is her OB-GYN, and what will the delivery hospital be? Our surrogate, Melissa, wanted to use the OB-GYN who delivered her two babies. He turned out to be a wonderful doctor, and the delivering hospital was also wonderful, with a top tier Neonatal Intensive Care Unit. However, at the time, we did not do much research on the doctor nor the hospital. In retrospect, we should have. This is good information for you to know, and if for some reason you wish for your surrogate to use a different OB-GYN and deliver at a different hospital than she wants, this is an important conversation to have when choosing your surrogate.

- Is she a first-time surrogate or a repeat surrogate? Melissa was a first-time surrogate, and she got pregnant on the first embryo transfer and carried our daughter, Ava, to full term. We were a little nervous to choose a surrogate who had not been a surrogate before—the whole proven surrogate versus unknown. But we ultimately felt so good about her, and so did our fertility doctor, that we felt 100 percent confident that Melissa would be the surrogate for us. There are definitely some pros and cons to choosing a first-time surrogate versus a repeat surrogate. It's best to talk through this with your fertility doctor, who can weigh in based on your specific situation. For example, if you only have one embryo, your doctor might suggest a repeat, proven surrogate in order to help reassure you should the embryo transfer not work that it was not because your surrogate was a first-time surrogate.

- Does she have health insurance that will cover the surrogacy pregnancy? The first trimester, you will pay your fertility doctor out of pocket. But when your surrogate gets released to the OB-GYN, then *her* insurance will be used. If her health insurance will not cover the surrogacy pregnancy, then you will need to purchase a health insurance policy for her to use. This will cost you more money. You can work with your surrogacy agency to get you a quote for how much extra money you will be spending if you need to purchase your surrogate a policy. I mention this as part of what you should know when considering how much money you will need for the surrogacy.

As an addition to this list of things for you to consider when choosing your ideal surrogate, I suggest that you first ask your fertility doctor what he/she is looking for in your surrogate. Based on your specific situation, your doctor might have a specific list of criteria for you to consider in choosing a surrogate. Your fertility doctor will also have required criteria for your surrogate's BMI, her previous pregnancy histories, and more.

Medical Considerations

In Vitro Fertilization (IVF)

If you are like me and had to undergo tons of infertility treatments, then you will know all about this when it comes time for your surrogate to undergo IVF. I was able to tell Melissa what the hormone shots were like and give her tips, like to ice the injection area before administering a shot. I was the "expert" on the IVF part, and she, based on her prior experience of carrying and giving birth to two children of her own, was the "expert" on carrying and having the baby. If the same is true for you and your surrogate, you can support each other at these parts in the surrogacy process.

The Appointments

The medical appointments can feel awkward, including due to things like where to stand, what to say, etc. I recommend that you let your surrogate get weighed in private and get undressed and covered up before you enter the exam room. Also, allow her time to talk to the doctor in private. For example, she might have a question about sex that she would feel uncomfortable asking in front of you. You should also ensure that your surrogate signs forms giving you access to the OB and to the pregnancy medical records.

Tour the Delivery Hospital

If you can, tour the delivery hospital. Ask the OB when a good time to take a tour would be and then schedule one. We went on a tour with Melissa. She already knew the hospital because she delivered her kids there, but it was nice to all be together and ask all of our questions at one time. It made me feel a lot more comfortable having toured the hospital ahead of time.

Have a Birth Plan

Work with your surrogacy agency and your surrogate and discuss a birth plan. For example, who will be in the room during the delivery, where does everyone stand, who cuts the cord, who will do skin-to-skin first among the intended parents, who goes in the room if there is a C-section, who does the baby go to if the intended parents miss the birth (etc.)? The more you can think about all of this and have a clear understanding and expectation among all of the involved parties, the better for everyone.

The Birth

Do your best to be at the birth. It is an absolutely unbelievably beautiful experience! The following is a list of things to consider in relation to the birth.

- Your attorney should mail the originals of the legal documents to your hospital, but it is a good idea to bring an extra original version with you. Also, be sure your surrogate brings an extra copy with her.

- Hopefully you will get your own hospital room to be with the baby in post-birth. But I suggest you have contingency plans in place should the hospital not have a room for you. This is something you can figure out with your agency and the hospital ahead of time.

- Make sure you spend time with your surrogate in the hospital. Let her hold the baby. Take pictures together. You can even frame her a photo of all of you with the baby and mail it to her later. Your surrogate will love this!

- We also brought a special gift for our surrogate and her family along with a handwritten note. And my mom brought her flowers.

- Make sure you all say goodbye to one another before you leave the hospital. Then text your surrogate when you get home so that she knows you are all home safe and sound.

Communication

Communication is key to a successful surrogacy pregnancy and experience. Usually, your surrogate is someone you do not yet know, and you want to feel comfortable with her and develop a trusting relationship. The beginning stages of your relationship can feel like dating and can be uncomfortable. As the intended parents, you take the lead in the relationship and model the relationship based on what you would like. For example, do you want more of a texting relationship than a speaking or in-person one? Do you want weekly Skype or FaceTime calls with her? Establishing this pattern and expectation right at the beginning of the relationship with your surrogate will help set the tone for how and when you communicate.

Also, don't have every communication with your surrogate solely be about the pregnancy. Ask her about her weekend plans, how her kids are doing, etc. Get to know her as a person. Acknowledge holidays and special occasions that occur like Christmas, her birthday, her kids' birthdays, and Mother's Day. Little gifts and cards are wonderful. If you travel, make sure your surrogate knows where you are and how to best reach you. If your phone won't be working, make sure she knows other ways to contact you. If you are able to attend a medical appointment with her, ask her to go to lunch after the appointment. All these types of things help deepen your connection and relationship. Open communication is a must. With surrogacy, you cannot control anything, but the more you can do to connect with your surrogate, the more comfortable you will be with her.

I also want to emphasize the importance of communication in general during surrogacy, not just communication with your surrogate. As the intended parent, you will still need to take the lead in communication with all of your professionals. Be in charge. Yes, you are paying everyone a lot of money to do their jobs, but it is still best to take the lead and communicate, ask questions, etc.

Other Considerations

Remember, IT'S YOUR PREGNANCY, TOO! Do things like register for gifts, have a baby shower, decorate the baby's room (unless you are superstitious about any of this), and more. You are having a baby, and you should enjoy your "pregnancy" as much as any other parent-to-be would.

* * *

MELISSA'S TIPS

If there are two main points I would emphasize to all potential intended parents, they are these: communication and trust. Communication usually leads to a trusting relationship, so be as open and honest with your surrogate as possible. Check in—let her know you are thinking about her and that you care. Keep in mind, too, that ALL surrogates have their own families and lives, so if they don't respond right away, be patient. Every surrogate I have talked to is very aware of how difficult the surrogacy process is for intended parents and has tried to be as warm and accommodating to the intended parents' fears and needs as possible. So, don't be afraid to talk to your surrogate about those things. More likely than not, your surrogate will be more than willing to communicate with you as often as you like. Every person likes to know that someone is thinking about them. So, even just a sweet, quick text can mean the world to your surrogate.

It is also very helpful to be upfront about what is important to you throughout the different aspects of the surrogacy journey. I know sometimes it is hard to know until you are in it, but you should really take the time to think about things like communication (how often?), visits (which appointments will you likely try to attend?), delivery (how do you envision things going in the delivery room?), and communication after birth. Not every surrogate is hoping to become best friends with their intended parents, but almost all at least want updates or to check in every once in a while after delivery. So being upfront about your expectations with that is key to a good match.

Appendix B

Tips for Surrogates

EMILY'S TIPS

From my perspective of having been an intended parent, the following is a (non-exhaustive) list of things for surrogates or potential surrogates to consider about the surrogacy process.

- Do not keep anything from your intended parents. If you are not sure how to say something to your intended parents, consult your surrogacy agency or attorney to assist you.

- Follow ALL doctor's orders exactly. If you have any questions at all about how to administer medications and hormones, ask and ask again.

- If your intended parents cannot make a doctor appointment, offer to Skype or FaceTime them into the appointment, video the heartbeat during the heartbeat appointment and send the video to them, and even video what the doctor is saying. And text or call them with an update right after you leave the appointment. As much as you can help keep the intended parents in the know and involved, the better.

- Consult your intended parents about dates, days of the week, times, etc. that would work best for them to make doctor appointments, whether they intend to join the appointments in person, by phone, or by Skype or FaceTime.

- Remember your intended parents' story, struggles, fears, and anxieties in their journey to their baby.

- Respond to your intended parents in a timely manner. If you get a text from them, for example, and you are too busy at the moment, still reply quickly and say that you will get back to them as soon as possible.

- At doctor appointments, the nurses and other personnel may refer to you as "mom." Please correct them—it makes us intended parents feel good!

- Talk to your surrogacy agency to see if there is anything it knows the intended parents would like you to do for them, like take weekly bump pictures and give them an album of the pictures after the birth. For some intended parents, this might be sensitive, so it is best to ask your agency first.

And your agency might have other ideas for you.

- Ask your intended parents how they want to be told when you are in labor. Do they want to know as soon as you have contractions, even if it's a false alarm? What if it's the middle of the night—do they want to be notified then? Do they want to be called as soon as you feel a tiny contraction or, instead, when you are further along? We told our surrogate, Melissa, we wanted to be called any time of the day or night with any sign of contractions. We told her, even if we had a dozen false alarms, we want to at least be in the know to help guarantee we would not miss the birth. And, if your intended parents live further away from you, you can help them know what hotels are close to the hospital so that they can travel to you for the birth.

* * *

MELISSA'S TIPS

Choosing Your Surrogacy Agency

The number one thing I looked for in a surrogacy agency was its experience. I did a ton of research on surrogacy in general before deciding to sign up to be a surrogate. One thing I specifically researched were horror stories—surrogacy gone wrong. I wanted to know everything that could go wrong so that I could be as prepared as possible.

While doing this research, there was one common thread between all of the "bad" stories of surrogacy—not using an experienced agency or not using an agency at all. At that point, I knew that "experience" would be my number one consideration in choosing an agency.

Other things I looked for in a surrogacy agency, after experience, was its involvement in the LGBTQ community, the support it offered to its surrogates, and its ratings from other surrogates. All these things were very important to me. Obviously, you need to decide what is important to *you*, personally; but I strongly feel that experience should be important to anyone considering becoming a surrogate.

After narrowing down my search to a few agencies, I started reaching out by email to ask a few questions. I wanted to see who would be responsive. Surprisingly, there were two large agencies that never responded to me. Of course, they got crossed off my list immediately. I wanted an agency that valued me and my questions and was going to be, at the very least, responsive! That left me with two agencies, and, at that point, I made my decision based on referrals from former surrogates and which agency was most experienced. The agency I chose was the best for me, and I have never regretted it for a second.

Now would be a good time to mention a big, important tip for your surrogacy journey: utilize your agency and everything it has to offer. All agencies work differently, but I always knew if I needed anything, I could reach out to my case manager, my counselor, or my trust coordinator and whatever question or concern I had would be handled. I see many surrogates go through something (whether it be in their personal or professional life, or as a part of their surrogacy journey) and they just suffer in silence or don't think it is something they need to bother anyone with. The agency is there for you and can help you with just about anything. Don't be afraid to utilize the help that is provided to you (and that your intended parents are paying for!).

Choosing Your Intended Parents

The best advice I can give for choosing your intended parents is to be very open, take your time, and go with your gut. Working with surrogates now, in a professional capacity, I tell them all the same thing: you could receive two profiles or five, and you will have a hard time choosing—at first. But read them all, discuss them with your significant other (if applicable), and then read them all again. At that point, walk away and take a night to sleep on it. Nine times out of ten, your brain will not stop bringing you back to one particular couple, and that is how you know *they* are the intended parents for you.

Also, don't rule anyone out just because they didn't fit some preconceived idea you had in your head about your intended parents. Most surrogates picture a married couple with no children, but there are plenty of intended parents out there who are single or who have children and for whatever reason need you to help them complete their family. Those journeys can be just as rewarding as giving two-partner intended parents their first child. So, you may need time to shift your ideals and the picture you had in your head, but, do that, and you might find the intended parent(s) you choose to be much different than what you had planned. And it might be the best decision of your life!

Medical Considerations

One thing surrogates need to be prepared for before embarking on the surrogacy journey is how different it will be from their own pregnancies. There will be many more medications, appointments, ultrasounds, and blood draws than when you had your own children naturally. In Vitro Fertilization (IVF) is a different beast, and even though you might have conceived with ease, it does not mean that will happen with the surrogacy as well.

At the beginning of the surrogacy process, you will meet with the reproductive endocrinologist (RE) chosen by your intended parents. This is who will clear you to be a surrogate (after running tests, checking blood work, and performing ultrasounds), do the embryo transfer, and monitor you after confirmation of pregnancy. A surrogate needs to be prepared that she will not be seeing her OB right from the start. A RE is a doctor who specializes in IVF and infertility, so that is where you need to start. Once you are cleared by the RE, you will start medication.

A couple of tips to keep in mind for the medication injections are to change sides of your body and change location every time you inject. The nurse at the office will show you how and give you a ton of tips. Utilize your RE's nurse! The nurse can help with any questions or concerns that you have, so be sure you get the nurse's direct line or email after your first appointment. It also helps many to ice the injection site before an injection to numb the area, and then to use heat, rubbing, and walking after the injection to help disperse the medication (progesterone especially). Another important thing to mention is, don't expect the medications to end when you get that pregnancy confirmation. Depending on the RE, you will continue progesterone for anywhere from six to twelve weeks gestation. Many surrogates are shocked, frustrated, or annoyed by this, so definitely keep that in mind going into the medication phase of surrogacy.

Once you are released to your OB, for the most part, everything should be very similar to your prior pregnancies. You might have to see a maternal-fetal medicine doctor (MFM), who is essentially a specialist for high-risk pregnancies. Many OBs consider any IVF pregnancy high-risk, so be prepared if they want to refer you to get checked out by an MFM.

My final tip is to be your own advocate—always. Yes, this is not your baby, and of course the parents should be part of important discussions. But, ultimately, as long as the baby's health is never in question, the decisions about delivery are made between you and your OB. It is usually a requirement that you must deliver in a hospital with a certified OB (unless you and your intended parents agree to something else during the contract phase), but how you get to that step is a decision you make with your OB.

Communication

There is no right or wrong way to communicate with your intended parents. Every relationship is different, and they form in different ways. The one thing you should always do is respond when the intended parents reach out to you. Be very in tune with the fact that it is so hard for them to be disconnected from their child like this, and you are their only connection to their child. So, if they want an update or just to see how you are feeling, respond and let them know. If it gets to be too much, talk to them about it. Most intended parents will understand that you still have your own life and might not be able to talk three times a day! Just be open and honest with them if it gets to be too much.

And always update your intended parents with ANY news. Even if you had a quick in and out OB appointment, don't wait for them to ask for the update; instead, give them a quick text or quick phone call to let them know how it went. But, overall, the relationship will form the best way that works for all parties involved, so be as flexible as you can to make that happen.

About the Authors

EMILY DUBIN FIELD is a mom thanks to IVF and surrogacy. It was a long, hard, and emotional road for her to finally become a mom. She is very open about her fertility journey and feels that, when you go through something difficult in life, who better than you to do something about it for others? She has her MBA in nonprofit management and has dedicated her career to making a difference in the world. Emily and her husband Gregg started Field Fertility in 2016, which is a legal and consulting business working with intended parents, surrogates, egg donors, sperm donors, and embryo donors. Field Fertility is a member of the Society of Ethics of Egg Donation and Surrogacy, American Bar Association, American Society for Reproductive Medicine, Resolve, Men Having Babies, and Family Equality and is a supporter of Feit 4 Kidz Fertility Fund by JFLA and Baby Quest Foundation. Emily may be contacted at: emily@fieldfertility.com and at www.fieldfertility.com.

MELISSA FLECK currently spends her time as a mom to two very active kids, is a wife to a hardworking law enforcement officer, and is an active member of the surrogacy community. She has been working at the Center for Surrogate Parenting, Inc. since 2016, where she is a surrogate case manager. Having been a surrogate herself, she gets to pay it forward by interviewing and guiding potential surrogates on their surrogacy journey, working for the same agency that brought her and her intended parent and coauthor, Emily, together. Melissa also enjoys working out at her local boot camp-style gym, watching her kids play sports, attending Dodgers games, spending time with friends and extended family, and watching as many movies as she can.

CPSIA information can be obtained
at www.ICGtesting.com
Printed in the USA
LVHW051230020520
654894LV00020B/1966

9 781734 034400

5/20